Forever Young
Fitness Drinks

Protein:

Keeps body, mind, and spirit fit

The Power Fuel

Every aspect of our bodies, including both our physical and our mental health, is determined by protein. Nutrients such as vitamins, trace elements, minerals, fatty acids, and carbohydrates are merely auxiliary materials that help activate the protein. From the 24 amino acids that you must consume every day, your body assembles around 50,000 different proteins: Your immune system, your muscles, your hormones, your emotions, your life.

PROTEIN DEFICIENCY DESPITE EXCESS

Protein is abundantly present in our normal diet. Not only is it contained in fish, lean meat, poultry, low-fat cheese and milk products, but also in vegetables, whole grains, and legumes. Nevertheless, many people suffer from a protein deficiency. They utilize protein badly. If you don't absorb enough nutrients, if you eat too much fat or too much sugar, protein never reaches its place of effectiveness, the 70 billion cells in your body. Your mind slows down and your immune system weakens, your body stores globs of fat, your muscles dwindle, your skin ages, and your organs lose their capacity to perform.

The Most Valuable Ingredient

If you weigh 150 pounds, 30 of those pounds are pure protein, including your hair, bones and joints, enzymes and hormones, muscles, immune system, and blood. Protein is truly the most valuable ingredient in your food, the building blocks from which your life, moods, and energy are constructed. What you eat each day must supply your body with a booster shot of protein that it can use to produce hormones, keep your immune system up and running, build up muscles, and repair cells. But whether the protein actually reaches its place of effectiveness, the cells, can be seen only by looking at your blood. The average person's blood protein level is low, resulting in fragile bones, weak muscles, a lack of red, oxygen-carrying blood cells, a listless immune system, and an unsteady psyche. People with a high blood protein level are life's winners. Nothing keeps them down.

How Much Protein Do You Have In Your Blood?

A low protein content indicates that your body is running on half steam. With a blood protein level of:

* 8 g/dl you feel good and are active;
* 7 g/dl you feel pretty good;
* 6 g/dl you're tired and without energy.

Ask your doctor to tell you your level.

Fill Up Your Protein Tank

When you have a lot of protein in your blood, you become more alert, you have better concentration, and you're happier. So raise your protein level to the top of the normal range. To do this, you'll have to fill your body up with protein over the course of several weeks. Too much all at once won't help you. Your body eliminates the surplus, causing damage to your kidneys. So give your body only a small dose of extra protein each day, just enough to refill its empty stores. The ideal is one serving of protein every four hours because it takes the protein four hours to pass through your kidneys and exit your body. It's a somewhat tedious process but just consider the rewards: Vitality, lust for life, and energy!

How Much Protein Does a Person Need?

At least 20 percent of the calories you consume in a day should be in the form of protein. It is estimated that you need about 0.8 grams of protein per 2 pounds of body weight. Therefore a person weighing 130 pounds has a minimum requirement of 48 grams. However, athletes, people with high-stress jobs, and people with an overall low blood protein level need more protein—up to twice as much.

Magic
Create energy and good moods
Amino Acids

There are ten amino acids that are especially important to your body—your body can't produce these amino acids on its own or can produce only to a limited extent. If you don't get them from your diet, the other amino acids are also rendered useless, like a house missing its beams.

LEUCINE KEEPS YOU FIT

Leucine is an important building block in blood protein and tissues. This amino acid is essential for muscular stamina and physical performance. If you don't have enough, your entire body is weakened.

ISOLEUCINE COMBATS STRESS

Isoleucine is essential for muscular stamina and works as a brain-activating amino acid. This amino acid mainly produces neurotransmitters (chemicals that transmit messages for the brain) that protect you against stress.

LYSINE KEEPS YOU YOUNG

As a component of collagen, lysine keeps your skin firm and protects your arteries from sclerosis. As a building block of enzymes, lysine stimulates the growth hormone (the physiological fountain of youth), which builds up muscle and burns off fat. Without lysine, there are no enzymes to fight cancer cells. Lysine is also a component of carnitine, the nutrient that channels fat to the cells, thus making fat combustion possible. Lysine strengthens your resistance to viruses and can help those suffering from a lack of drive or difficulty concentrating.

METHIONINE—METABOLISM'S JACK OF ALL TRADES

Methionine is the starting point for all protein synthesis. This amino acid is a component of carnitine, which transports fat to the cells where it is combusted. Methionine is important for the defense function (phagocytic ability) of the killer cells in the blood. It also protects our body's detoxifier, the liver.

THREONINE PERKS UP WEARY SOULS

Threonine is the key substance in the production of the endothelial relaxing factor, meaning that it is essential for dilating the blood vessels and, thus, for the flow of blood through the body, heart, and brain. A deficiency often results in constricted blood vessels, fatigue, and even heart trouble.

Phenylalanine Lifts Spirits and Stops Hunger

This amino acid is a basic material for mood elevating hormones such as norepinephrine, ACTH, dopamine, and endorphins. Phenyl-alanine helps relieve depression and build self-esteem. It's also used as a pain remedy for arthritis, rheumatism, and muscular pain. In the intestines, phenylalanine helps regulate cholecystokinin, the hormone that signals the brain when you're full.

Tryptophan Relaxes

The body uses tryptophan to produce melatonin, the fountain-of-youth hormone, as well as serotonin, the chief hormone for inner peace, equanimity, and happiness. When you're under stress, anxious or having difficulty sleeping, or if you want to quit smoking, take an extra helping of tryptophan. A deficiency can result in depression and even psychoses.

Valine Peps Up Nerves and Your Immune System

Valine promotes the healthy functioning of your nervous system and aids in the production of hemoglobin, the red blood pigment that transports revitalizing oxygen to all your cells. Valine is also important for building up an active immune system.

Histidine Puts the Wind in Your Sails

Histidine is also required for producing the oxygen-carrying red hemoglobin. In other words, the more histidine you have, the better you perform, both physically and mentally. Histidine regulates cell growth and regeneration. The cells' tiny power plants, the mitochondria, require this amino acid for transporting oxygen and, therefore, for producing power.

Taurine Keeps You Thin

This protein material is important for over-eaters and food lovers because taurine increases fat combustion by a factor of four. And taurine detoxifies the liver whenever it suffers a toxic overload (such as from alcohol). This amino acid also blocks the unpleasant effects of caffeine by slowing down your pulse.

Eat Protein with

Stay fit and trim

Little or No Fat

Is too much protein a bad thing? Certainly "too much" of anything is bad, even too much oxygen. We can't live without oxygen, but when there's too much it becomes toxic. The question is, how much is too much? Your body is made up of about 30 pounds of protein. Every day you lose a handful of it, from 2 to 4 ounces, and every day you have to replenish it.

Most people have a low protein level even when they eat a huge amount of protein, usually in the form of meat. The problem is that the protein on your plate never reaches the places where you need it most, the places in your body where the tiny protein building blocks, the amino acids, work to raise your spirits, repair cells, mobilize your immune system, build up your muscles, and get your power hormones moving. And why doesn't it reach its destination? First of all, because you lack the vital nutrients required for digesting protein. Nutritious protein is lying inert in your intestines, bloating you, and causing allergies.

Secondly, because you eat protein with fat. If you really want to fill up your tank with protein power, you need to eat protein on its own, without the fat. Fat prevents the valuable amino acids from participating in metabolism, starting in your intestines. Fat hinders peristalsis, the movement of the intestines. It takes only a minimal amount of fat to delay the absorption of protein into the bloodstream by several hours. The amino acids barely trickle into your bloodstream and can't reach their place of effectiveness fast enough or in large enough quantities to do you any good. Unless the correct amount of protein is made available all at once, your body can never activate sufficient quantities of hormones and neurotransmitters, elevate your brain to a state of euphoria, render your thoughts crystal-clear, fill you full of self-confidence, or help you achieve your highest level of performance. Where can you find protein with little or no fat? Valuable sources include tender fish, lean poultry, cottage cheese, yogurt, and other low-fat dairy products, as well as legumes. But since you can't have a plateful of these foods every four hours, I suggest that you also use a high-quality protein powder, preferably in combination with fruit or vegetables. Fruits and vegetables provide the nutrients you need to transport the protein to the 70 billion cells in your body, making you thin and happy, healthy and fit, stress-proof and creative, youthful and beautiful.

Protein Powder from the Store

Because protein is almost always combined with fat, you can seldom consume enough protein to fill up your empty stores without simultaneously broadening your hips. So go to the health food store and buy protein without fat. A good protein powder is an excellent means of raising your blood protein level. After only a few days you will see—or rather feel—that you have more power, your thoughts are clearer, and your mood simply couldn't be better.

Important: If you fill up your tank with protein powder, you also need to drink a lot of liquid—at least three quarts a day.

A Good Powder

A protein powder from the health food store is "good" if it contains 60 percent animal protein (usually from egg whites and milk) and 40 percent plant protein (frequently soy). You'll know it's high-quality if it says "biological value over 100" on the label. In addition, an extra serving of carnitine in the protein powder helps you lose weight. Added vitamins and minerals will ensure an efficient protein metabolism and help fill up empty vital nutrient tanks.

Protein Powder as a Fitness Drink

As an accompaniment to a healthy low-sugar, low-fat diet, consuming one or two of our fitness drinks every day will help you fill up your empty tanks.

Naturally, you can also simply dissolve the powder in water or low-fat milk. But then make sure you also eat some fruit or vegetables because these foods contain the active ingredients that render the protein biologically active in your body. But why not go ahead and combine them, especially when they can taste so delicious?

Power
Losing weight with protein drinks
Week

You can lose a pound a day by stimulating the fat burning process with exercise, protein, and vital nutrients. The lack of these three elements is the sole reason why so many people today are overweight. No diet can help you achieve long-term weight loss. On the contrary, if you starve yourself, your body will attack your muscles and consume the only organs that burn fat. But you can prevent this by running 30 minutes every day—easily, without stress and with a smile—and by consuming protein, which prevents your body from breaking down muscle mass. Protein is also responsible for fat being sucked out of the fat cells and burned. Especially when you're trying to lose weight, your body needs protein that it can invest in muscles and fat burning hormones, such as the growth hormone HGH that builds muscles and melts fat. Another important factor is vital nutrients. We would all have a higher fat metabolism if our diet contained enough vital nutrients. Vitamin C boosts fat combustion, but this is also true of vitamin B6, magnesium, iodine, chromium, and selenium.

How to Melt Away the Fat

Prepare: Buy a good pair of running shoes and a pulse monitor. Ask your doctor whether it's safe for you to run and diet.

Run: Run 30 minutes every morning and evening, keeping your pulse below 140.

Consume protein: Drink three fitness drinks per day. For suggestions, see the next page.

Drink: Drink three quarts of water each day. Tea and vegetable juices are also permitted, but don't drink alcohol.

Consider a supplement: Choose a good multivitamin-mineral preparation. This will stimulate fat metabolism, fill up empty stores, and prevent deficiencies.

Fill up on fruit: In addition to the fruit drinks, you can also feast on pure fruit—as much as you want and whatever you want. The best are the tropical fruits and whatever fruits are in season.

Maintain your weight: Once you've lost enough weight, continue to run 30 minutes every day. If you can maintain your weight for three to six months, you're home free!

PLAN FOR THE WEEK

Monday

❋ Strawberry-Pineapple Mix ❋ Melon Shake ❋ Tomato-Avocado Drink

Tuesday

❋ Papaya-Orange Shake ❋ Cherry-Buttermilk Drink ❋ Icy Cucumber-Dill Drink

Wednesday

❋ Mango-Coconut Drink ❋ Chocolate-Pear Shake ❋ Carrot-Herb Shake

Thursday

❋ Kiwi-Grapefruit Drink with Mint ❋ Apricot-Almond Shake ❋ Mango-Carrot Mix

Friday

❋ Apple-Elderberry Drink ❋ Citrus-Buttermilk Flip ❋ Spicy Vegetable Shake

Saturday

❋ Berry Smoothie ❋ Banana-Yogurt Drink ❋ Kiwi-Avocado Mix

Sunday

❋ Peach Melba Cocktail ❋ C-Packed Blueberry Shake ❋ Celery Root Spinach Flip

Six reasons why it's worth switching on the blender

1. *Protein power:* Your protein tanks are empty. Replenish your stores with fitness drinks.
2. *Fat burning power:* Fitness drinks supply all the vital nutrients with few calories.
3: *Muscle power:* Protein prevents your body from taking away from your immune system to build up your muscles.
4. *Brain doping:* It's best to fill up your empty nutrient stores in the morning. Your brain will then have an ample supply to support serenity, creativity, and flashes of genius.
5. *Cell rejuvenation:* Our drinks contain all the nutrients your 70 billion cells need to renew themselves again and again.
6: *Good mood material:* Protein and nutrients from fruit or vegetables provide the basis for the happy messengers. Your body starts producing more serotonin and endorphins.

Seasonal Calendar

Fruits with enzymes are best

# of Fruit

IN PRAISE OF FRUIT

Do you eat fruit five times a day? If you answered no, you should start doing so now. Nothing provides you with more vital nutrients and healthy energy than fresh fruit from the Garden of Eden.

Fruit nourishes your thoughts because its fructose provides steady reinforcements for the brain without putting stress on your blood sugar level. Vital nutrients in fruit help to prevent fatigue, sharpen your concentration, and raise your spirits through the production of hormones.

Fruit keeps you thin. Its vitamin C, minerals, and phytochemicals boost fat metabolism and clean out the body by way of the kidneys. Fruit's fiber sets sluggish digestion in motion and carries toxins out of the intestines.

Fruit is medicine and has been used as such for millennia. Its vital nutrients strengthen your organs, aid in blood production, steady your nerves, and keep your digestive glands up and running. Fruit helps lower your blood pressure and keep your blood fat values low. It fortifies your immune system, purifies your intestines, cleans out all your blood vessels, and strengthens connective tissue in your skin and blood vessels. Fruit protects you against cancer, heart attacks, and strokes, mitigates asthma symptoms, and slows down the aging process. It helps you fall asleep and works against migraines. It strengthens your bones, raises your libido, and makes your hair shine. One thing's for certain: There's a fruit for every complaint; you just have to pluck it five times a day.

A tip for fitness and eternal youth: Every day, make yourself a large bowl of fruit salad using whatever fruits are in season.

SEASONAL CALENDAR

	Jan	Feb	March	April	May	June	July	Aug	Sept	Oct	Nov	Dec
Apples	✽	✽	✽	✽	✽	✽	✽	✽	✽	✽	✽	✽
Apricots					✽	✽	✽	✽	✽			
Avocados	✽	✽	✽	✽	✽	✽	✽	✽	✽	✽	✽	✽
Bananas	✽	✽	✽	✽	✽	✽	✽	✽	✽	✽	✽	✽
Blackberries						✽	✽	✽	✽	✽		
Blueberries						✽	✽	✽	✽			
Cherries					✽	✽	✽	✽				
Currants						✽	✽	✽				
Dates	✽	✽	✽	✽	✽	✽	✽	✽	✽	✽	✽	✽
Elderberries									✽	✽	✽	
Figs (fresh)	✽	✽	✽	✽	✽	✽	✽	✽	✽	✽	✽	✽
Gooseberries					✽	✽	✽	✽				
Grapefruit	✽	✽	✽	✽	✽	✽	✽	✽	✽	✽	✽	✽
Grapes	✽	✽						✽	✽	✽	✽	✽
Kiwis	✽	✽	✽	✽	✽	✽	✽	✽	✽	✽	✽	✽
Mangos	✽	✽	✽	✽	✽	✽	✽	✽	✽	✽	✽	✽
Melon	✽	✽	✽	✽	✽	✽	✽	✽	✽	✽	✽	✽
Oranges	✽	✽	✽	✽	✽	✽	✽	✽	✽	✽	✽	✽
Papaya	✽	✽	✽	✽	✽	✽	✽	✽	✽	✽	✽	✽
Peaches	✽	✽	✽	✽	✽	✽	✽	✽	✽			
Pears	✽	✽	✽	✽	✽	✽	✽	✽	✽	✽	✽	✽
Pineapple	✽	✽	✽	✽	✽	✽	✽	✽	✽	✽	✽	✽
Plums	✽	✽	✽	✽	✽	✽	✽	✽	✽	✽		
Raspberries						✽	✽	✽	✽			
Strawberries	✽	✽	✽	✽	✽	✽	✽	✽			✽	✽
Tangerines	✽	✽	✽							✽	✽	✽

✽ These dots indicate the months when the fruit is available.

✽ These dots indicate the high season for each fruit.

Berry
Soothing fitness drink
Smoothie

Rinse the berries briefly. Remove the stems from the berries and put them
in a blender. Add the maple syrup and orange juice and blend thoroughly
for fifteen seconds.

Cut the frozen banana into several pieces. Add the banana,
protein powder, and water to the blender and blend vigorously
for an additional fifteen seconds.

Pour the mixture into a frosted cocktail glass. Serve the drink
with a straw.

Tip: To frost the cocktail glass, place it in the refrigerator or
freezer for several hours ahead of time, or fill the glass with
crushed ice and let it stand briefly.

Serves 1:
3 oz mixed berries
2 tsp maple syrup
2 tbs orange juice
1 medium banana, frozen
2 tbs protein powder
1/2 cup cold mineral water

 Berries

In Asia, these small spherical fruits are considered to be
a folk remedy. They're jam-packed with vitamins and
minerals. Berries' essential oils, pigments, and tannins
fill you with energy, calm your nerves, and render you
fit and relaxed. Their flavones protect you from cancer.
In addition to boosting your metabolism, berries
fortify your immune system, strengthen your heart,
aid your kidneys in detoxifying your body, and help
prevent rheumatism, arthritis, and diabetes.

power

Mango-Coconut Drink

Tropical power for your cells

Peel and dice the mango. Set aside three nice mango cubes for garnish and place the remaining pieces in the blender.

Serves 1:
1 piece mango (about 4 oz)
1 lime
2 tsp brown coco sugar
1/4 cup cold unsweetened coconut milk
2 tbs protein powder
1/2 cup cold unfiltered apple juice
1-2 tbs grated coconut

Remove a spiral-shaped strip of zest from the lime and set it aside. Squeeze out the lime juice and add the lime juice, sugar, and coconut milk to the blender. Blend vigorously for fifteen seconds.

Add the protein powder and apple juice. Blend thoroughly for an additional ten seconds.

Moisten the rim of a large glass with water, turn the glass upside-down, and dip the rim into the grated coconut. Place ice cubes in the glass and pour the contents of the blender over the top. Thread the reserved mango cubes onto a cocktail skewer and lay them across the rim of the glass. Garnish with the lime zest. Serve the drink with a straw.

Coconut

This cannonball of minerals (mainly magnesium, iron, sodium, and selenium) protects your heart, calms your nerves, and maintains your stomach and intestines. This exotic fruit also supplies valuable plant protein. Coconut is the ideal fruit for combating stress. In Southeast Asia it's prescribed for heartburn and gastritis.

power

Strawberry-

The skinny drink

Pineapple Mix

Wash the strawberries and set aside one nice berry for garnish. Remove the stems from the remaining berries and cut them into quarters.

Serves 1:
3 oz strawberries
2 tsp lemon juice
1 tsp floral honey
2/3 cup cold pineapple juice
2 tbs protein powder

Put the strawberries, lemon juice, honey, and half of the pineapple juice in a blender and blend thoroughly for fifteen seconds.

Add the protein powder and the remaining juice and blend for an additional ten seconds.

Pour the mixture into a tall glass. Cut partway into the reserved strawberry and place it on the rim of the glass for garnish. Serve the drink with a straw.

Strawberries

Strawberries make you thin while you eat. These small red balls of fitness provide more fat burning vitamin C than lemons and have almost no calories: 4 ounces contain less than 40 calories. Strawberries' super fiber pectin lowers your cholesterol level and another 300 ingredients make them precious medicine. Strawberries aid digestion, clean mucous membranes, reduce fevers, serve as a diuretic, boost metabolism, and even send bacteria scurrying.

power

Papaya-Orange

Morning dose of fitness

Shake

Peel the papaya and remove the seeds. Cut away a nice wedge of papaya and set it aside for garnish. Dice the remaining papaya and place it in a blender. Add the lime juice, honey, and half of the orange juice and blend for fifteen seconds. Add the protein powder and the remaining orange juice and blend for an additional ten seconds. Place two ice cubes in a large glass and pour in the contents of the blender. Cut partway into the reserved papaya wedge and lime slice and place them on the rim of the glass. Serve the drink with a straw.

Serves 1:

4 oz ripe papaya
1 tbs lime juice
1 tsp floral honey
1/2 cup cold freshly squeezed orange juice
2 tbs protein powder
1 lime slice

Papaya

There are many reasons to start your day with papaya. It stimulates digestion and pampers your body with beta carotene, the nutrient that protects your cells against premature aging. Papaya's calcium and potassium content arm you against stress.

power

Kiwi-Grapefruit

Reinforce your immune system

Drink with Mint

Set aside one nice kiwi slice for garnish. Peel the remaining kiwi, dice it, and put it in a blender. Set aside one small mint sprig. Remove the remaining mint leaves from the stems and cut them into fine strips. Add the mint leaves, lemon juice, maple syrup, and half of the grapefruit juice to the blender. Blend thoroughly for fifteen seconds. Add the protein powder and the remaining juice and blend for an additional ten seconds.

Serves 1:
1 kiwi (about 4 oz)
2 small sprigs fresh mint
2 tsp lemon juice
2 tsp maple syrup
2/3 cup cold grapefruit juice
2 tbs protein powder

Place ice cubes in a large glass and pour the kiwi mixture over the top. Cut partway into the reserved kiwi slice and place it on the rim of the glass. Garnish with the reserved mint sprig. Serve the drink with a straw.

Kiwi

This exotic green fruit has three times the vitamin C of citrus fruit. It also contains the enzyme actinidin, which helps the digestive system break down protein. Kiwi also benefits your immune system (which is made up of 3 1/2 lb of protein). Combined with grapefruit, it provides your immune system with an extra dose of power.

Peach Melba Cocktail

A cool cup

Serves 1:
3 oz fresh raspberries
2 tsp maple syrup
1 ripe peach (about 4 oz)
2 tsp lemon juice
2 tbs protein powder
1/2 cup cold mineral water
1 scoop vanilla frozen yogurt

Wash the raspberries, sort them, and set aside four or five nice berries for garnish. Put the remaining raspberries and 1 teaspoon of the maple syrup in a blender and purée the berries. Pour the berry purée into a large glass. Plunge the peach into a pot of boiling water for a few seconds to loosen the skin, then plunge it into a bowl of ice water. Remove the peach peel with a small knife. Cut the fruit in half, remove the pit, and cut the fruit into pieces. Put the peach, lemon juice, the remaining maple syrup, the protein powder, and half of the mineral water in the blender. Blend vigorously for fifteen seconds until the fruit is puréed.

Add the remaining mineral water and blend an additional ten seconds. Carefully pour the peach mixture over the puréed raspberries. Top with the frozen yogurt and garnish with the whole raspberries. Serve immediately with a spoon and fat straw.

Peaches

With its abundance of aromatics, these sweet, juicy stone fruits woo every palate. Peaches also beguile your nerves with B vitamins, satisfy your immune system with vitamin C, and pamper your bones with a concentrated charge of calcium.

Kiwi-Avocado

Green fitness cocktail

Mix

Serves 1:
2 oz ripe avocado
2 tbs lemon juice
1 kiwi (about 4 oz)
1 tsp brown sugar
1/2 cup cold mineral water
2 tbs protein powder
1 sprig fresh mint

Peel the avocado and chop the flesh, removing the pit. Put the avocado in a blender and drizzle with the lemon juice. Set aside one nice kiwi slice for garnish. Peel the remaining kiwi, chop it coarsely, and add it to the blender along with the sugar and half of the mineral water. Blend thoroughly for fifteen seconds. Add the protein powder and the remaining mineral water and blend thoroughly for an additional ten seconds.

Place ice cubes in a large glass and pour the avocado mixture over the top. Cut partway into the reserved kiwi slice and place on the rim of the glass. Garnish with the mint.

Avocados

Avocados provide unsaturated fatty acids that are essential to health. They moisturize your skin, lubricate cell walls, and fortify your nerves. Along with the finest oil, they supply nutritious protein. Avocados' true magic is in their mannoheptulose, a unique carbohydrate that lowers the blood sugar level. Eating avocados will make you feel alive, focused, and alert. And the vitamin E in avocados will also protect your heart.

power

White
Joyfully refreshing
Fruit Cocktail

Peel the orange and lemon slices, and chop the fruit. Peel the apple quarter, remove the core, and cut the fruit into small pieces. Wash and dice the peach. Put the prepared fruit and half of the grape juice in a blender and blend thoroughly for fifteen seconds.

Add the protein powder, cinnamon, and the remaining juice and blend for an additional ten seconds.

Put ice cubes in a large glass and pour the fruit mixture over the top. Wash the grapes, remove the stems, thread them onto a small wooden skewer, and lay it across the rim of the glass. Serve the drink with a fat straw.

Serves 1:
1 orange slice
1 lemon slice
1/4 tart apple
1/4 peach
2/3 cup cold white grape juice
2 tbs protein powder
2 pinches ground cinnamon
3 small seedless grapes

Apples

Apples provide you with several hundred nutrients. They stimulate digestion, drive away bacteria, pep up your immune system, and keep you thin. Organic acids help your liver to detoxify and pectin lowers your cholesterol level, as well as protecting your intestines and blood vessels. Start off your day with an apple and end it with one too. Apples contain nutrients that wake you up in the morning and relax you at night.

power

Apple-Elderberry Drink

Sweet medicine

Wash the apple and set aside a nice wedge for garnish. Peel the remaining apple, remove the core, cut the fruit into small pieces, and put it in a blender.

Serves 1:
About 3 oz tart apple
2 tsp lemon juice
2 tsp floral honey
1/3 cup cold unfiltered apple juice
2 tbs protein powder
1/4 cup cold elderberry juice (natural foods store)
1 sprig fresh mint

Add the lemon juice, honey and apple juice to the blender and blend the contents thoroughly for fifteen seconds.

Add the protein powder and elderberry juice and blend vigorously for an additional ten seconds. Place ice cubes in a large glass and pour the mixture over the top. Place the apple wedge on the rim of the glass. Garnish the drink with mint and serve with a straw.

Elderberries

Elderberries contain the trace element selenium, which gives you a joyful serenity, protects all your cells, and counteracts heavy metals. In addition, elderberry juice is better for colds than the popular hot lemon.

power

Persimmon-

An autumn cocktail

Orange Drink

Serves 1:

1/2 fully ripe Hachiya persimmon (about 4 oz)
1 tbs lime juice
2 tsp apple juice concentrate
1 tsp vanilla extract
2/3 cup freshly squeezed orange juice
2 tbs protein powder
1 tiny sprig fresh mint

Wash the persimmon, cut it in half, and set aside a nice wedge for garnish. Peel the remaining persimmon, remove the core, and chop the fruit. Put the persimmon, lime juice, and apple juice concentrate in a blender. Add the vanilla extract and half of the orange juice. Blend the mixture thoroughly for fifteen seconds.

Add the protein powder and the remaining juice and blend for an additional ten seconds. Pour the mixture into a large glass. Cut partway into the persimmon wedge and place it on the rim of the glass. Garnish the drink with mint and serve with a straw.

Persimmons

These fist-sized, sweet, orange berries taste like a cross between a tomato and an apricot. They're the ideal brain food. Each contains up to 20 percent glucose, an instant burst of energy for the brain. Like all tropical fruits, persimmons are chockfull of vitamins and are especially rich in skin-protecting vitamin A.

power

Black Currant-

Power for your nerves

Banana Shake

Peel the banana. Cut out a diagonal slice and set it aside for garnish.
Chop the remaining banana coarsely and put it in a blender along
with the lemon juice, honey, and half of the juice.
Blend thoroughly for fifteen seconds.
Add the protein powder and the remaining juice
and blend for an additional ten seconds.
Put ice cubes in a tall glass and pour the mixture
over the top. Cut halfway into the banana slice and
place it on the rim of the glass. Serve the drink with
a straw.

Serves 1:
1/2 medium banana
1 tbs lemon juice
2 tsp floral honey
2/3 cup cold black currant juice
(natural foods store)
2 tbs protein powder

Black Currants

A single black currant supplies no less than two
milligrams of vitamin C. This power vitamin works
in every cell as a biological catalyst for countless
enzymatic processes, including in fat combustion, in
the immune system, and in the production of hard
connective tissue. It also gives you firm skin and
elastic blood vessels. Above all, during stressful
times, black currant juice steadies your nerves. And
what makes these sour berries even sweeter is that
they contain pantothenic acid, the vitamin that
keeps your hair from turning gray.

power

Melon Shake

A cocktail for your heart

Using a melon baller, remove five nice balls from the melon. Set aside the melon balls
and a cut a wedge of melon for garnish. Peel the remaining melon, remove the seeds,
cut the flesh into pieces, and put them in a blender. Rinse the
mint and set aside a small sprig for garnish. Remove the
remaining mint leaves, wash them, chop, and add them to the
blender along with the apple juice concentrate and orange
juice. Blend the contents thoroughly for fifteen seconds.
Add the protein powder and milk and blend for an additional
ten seconds.

Place ice cubes in a tall glass and pour the blender contents
over the top. Thread the melon balls onto a cocktail skewer and lay them across the
rim of the glass with the melon wedge. Garnish with the reserved mint sprig. Serve
with a straw and a spoon.

Serves 1:

7 oz watermelon (or honeydew
or galia melon)
2 sprigs fresh mint
1 tbs apple juice concentrate
2 tbs orange juice
2 tbs protein powder
2/3 cup cold low-fat milk

Melons

Everyone knows that, with only 12 calories per 4 oz, melons
are the ideal slimming fruit. But what many people don't
know is that melons are recommended by American cancer
experts. This is because they contain large amounts of
carotenoids. Melons support your kidneys, help prevent
gout, and rheumatism and keep your blood thin. Researchers
have found that melons contain adenosine, a chemical that
acts like aspirin to prevent the clumping of blood platelets.

The beauty shake

Apricot-
Almond Shake

Wash the apricots, cut them in half, and remove the pits. Set aside a nice apricot wedge for garnish. Chop the remaining fruit coarsely and put it in a blender along with the apple juice concentrate, almond butter, and half of the milk. Blend vigorously for fifteen seconds. Add the remaining milk, protein powder, and vanilla extract. Blend briefly and vigorously.

Moisten the rim of a large glass with water, turn the glass upside-down, and dip the rim into the ground almonds. Put ice cubes in the glass and pour the apricot mixture over the top. Cut partway into the reserved apricot wedge and place it on the rim of the glass. Serve the drink with a fat straw.

Serves 1:
2-3 fresh apricots
(about 2 1/2 oz)
1 tbs apple juice concentrate
2 tsp almond butter
(natural foods store)
2/3 cup cold low-fat milk
2 tbs protein powder
1 tsp vanilla extract
1-2 tbs ground almonds

Apricots

The Hunzas, a people in the Himalayas, live long lives. This could be because they eat so many apricots, a fruit with an especially high carotinoid content. Carotinoids are a plant pigment that renders free radicals harmless, thus protecting your blood vessels, heart, and brain. Apricots contain the beauty vitamin pantothenic acid. They give you vitality and boost fat degradation. Apricots' silicic acid strengthens connective tissue, meaning that it firms up your skin. They also provide large amounts of potassium, a natural diuretic.

power

Citus-

Sweet and sour shake

Buttermilk Flip

Serves 1:
1 orange
1 lemon
2 tbs freshly squeezed pink grapefruit juice
1 egg yolk (optional)
1 tbs liquid fructose (natural foods store)
1/2 cup cold buttermilk
2 tbs protein powder

Cut a nice slice from both the orange, and lemon and set them aside for garnish. Peel the remaining orange, removing the white outer skin (pith). Cut the individual orange segments from their membranes, collecting the dripping juice. Place the orange segments and juice in a blender. Add the grapefruit juice, 1 tablespoon of the lemon juice, the egg yolk (if using), fructose, and half of the buttermilk. Blend the contents vigorously for fifteen seconds. Add the protein powder, a little finely grated zest from the lemon, and the remaining buttermilk and thoroughly blend for an additional ten seconds. Pour the mixture into a large glass. Cut partway into the reserved orange, and lemon slices and place them on the rim of the glass. Serve the drink with a straw.

Citrus Fruits

We've all experienced the eye-opening effects of vitamin C in the morning, in the form of orange juice. But few of us are aware that citrus's bioflavonoids (especially in the white skin) intensify the effects of the vitamin C. It's not necessary to be so meticulous about peeling when you eat citrus fruit.

power

Chocolate-Pear Shake

Fruit for your sweet tooth

Heat the milk until lukewarm. Meanwhile, wash the pear. Cut away a nice wedge of the pear and set it aside for garnish. Peel the remaining pear, remove the core, cut the flesh into pieces, and put it in a blender. Add the orange juice, apple juice concentrate, chocolate (setting a little aside for garnish), and half of the milk. Blend thoroughly for fifteen seconds. Add the protein powder and the remaining milk and blend thoroughly for an additional ten seconds.

Pour the mixture into a tall glass and place the pear wedge on the rim. Sprinkle the drink with the remaining chocolate and serve with a straw.

Serves 1:

2/3 cup low-fat milk
About 4 oz ripe pear
1 tsp orange juice
1 tsp apple juice concentrate
2 tbs finely grated unsweetened chocolate
2 tbs protein powder

Chocolate

Chocolate doesn't have to make you fat. If it's unsweetened chocolate and contains more than 60 percent cocoa, it doesn't affect insulin metabolism. Insulin, the fat storing hormone, stays locked away so that glucagon, the fat burning hormone, can break down the fat in the body. Interestingly cocoa beans supply more of the heart-protecting chemical polyphenol than a glass of red wine.

power

C-Packed

The drink of eternal youth

Blueberry Shake

Wash the fresh blueberries briefly, and pat dry or thaw the frozen

blueberries. Set aside ten nice berries for garnish. Place the remaining

berries, lemon juice, and kefir in a blender and blend

thoroughly for fifteen seconds.

Add the protein powder, ascorbic acid powder, and

milk and blend once more briefly and vigorously.

Pour the mixture into a tall glass. Thread the

reserved blueberries onto a cocktail skewer and lay

them across the rim of the glass. Serve the drink with

a fat straw.

Serves 1:
3 oz blueberries
(fresh or frozen)
1 tsp lemon juice
1/4 cup cold kefir
(natural foods store)
2 tbs protein powder
1 1/2 tsp ascorbic acid powder
1/2 cup cold low-fat milk

Blueberries

Blueberries are nature's lifestyle pills. They contain
an entire pharmacy of bioactive ingredients. They
help prevent cancer, fortify the immune system,
lower cholesterol and blood fat levels, and relieve
water retention. The tannins in blueberry skins
strengthen your intestines and their anthocyanin
(blue pigment) protects your cells, revitalizes
your body, and keeps you young. Blueberries are
the ideal accompaniment to kefir, the drink of
centenarians, supplemented by ascorbic acid
powder, pure vitamin C.

power

Cherry-Buttermilk
Purification cocktail
Drink

Wash the cherries and set aside a pair joined by their stems for garnish. Remove the pits from the remaining cherries and put the cherries in a

Serves 1:
4 oz sweet cherries
1 sprig fresh mint
1 tbs lemon juice
2 tsp apple juice concentrate
2 tbs protein powder
2/3 cup cold buttermilk

blender. Remove the leaves from the mint and set aside one or two nice leaves. Chop the remaining mint leaves and add them to the blender along with the lemon juice, apple juice concentrate, protein powder, and half of the buttermilk. Blend thoroughly for fifteen seconds.

Add the remaining buttermilk and blend thoroughly for an additional ten seconds. Pour the mixture into a tall glass, hang the reserved cherries over the rim of the glass, and garnish with the reserved mint leaves.

Cherries

Their minerals (potassium, iron, and calcium), vitamins (C and folic acid) and plant pigments (anthocyanin) purify, detoxify, boost connective tissue formation, stimulate blood production, prevent inflammation, and strengthen the immune system and bones. Cherry therapy rejuvenates you while it softens and cleanses your skin.

power

Apple-Nut Shake

For true happy hours

Toss 2 tablespoons of the hazelnuts in an ungreased skillet until they give off a toasted aroma. Remove the skillet from the heat. Wash the apple half and set aside a nice wedge for garnish. Peel the remaining apple, remove the core, chop the flesh, and put it in a blender. Add the lemon juice, cream, apple juice concentrate, and half of the milk and purée thoroughly for fifteen seconds.

Add the toasted hazelnuts, protein powder, and the remaining milk and blend for an additional ten seconds.

Brush a thin coating of honey onto the rim of a large glass and dip it into the remaining hazelnuts. Place ice cubes in the glass and fill with the apple-nut mixture. Serve with a straw.

Serves 1:

3 tbs finely grated hazelnuts
1/2 tart apple (about 4 oz)
1 tsp lemon juice
2 tbs cream
1 tbs apple juice concentrate
2/3 cup cold low-fat milk
2 tbs protein powder
Honey

Nuts

Studies worldwide show that combining simple unsaturated fatty acids with the vitamin E in nuts protects your heart and circulation and slows down the aging of your cells, especially your brain cells. And munching nuts raises your spirits because nuts supply tryptophan, the material from which your body produces the youth hormone melatonin and the happy hormone serotonin. Nuts provide many minerals and salicylic acids, which prevent the clumping of blood platelets and thus help prevent strokes.

power

Banana-

Fit-for-fun cocktail

Yogurt Drink

Peel the banana and set aside two slices for garnish. Coarsely chop
the remaining banana and place it in a blender. Add the lemon juice,
honey, yogurt, and half of the milk. Blend for
fifteen seconds.

Serves 1:
1 large, ripe banana
(about 4 oz)
1 tsp lemon juice
1 tbs floral honey
1/4 cup plain low-fat yogurt
1/2 cup cold low-fat milk
2 tbs protein powder
1 lemon slice

Add the protein powder and the remaining milk
and blend vigorously for an additional ten seconds.
Pour the drink into a tall glass. Thread the lemon
slice and banana slices onto a cocktail skewer and
place inside the glass. Serve the drink with a straw.

➤ Bananas

Bananas make you merry. Four ounces supply 1.7 grams
of serotonin. This important neurotransmitter makes
you serene and resistant to stress and puts you in a good
mood. It is a good fruit for people who lead high-stress
lives because it soothes gastric complaints and fortifies
mucous membranes. Eating something green before
banana's valuable starch has been broken down into
fructose and glucose helps process its nutrients.

power

Berry-Cherry
Shake

Steadies the nerves

Serves 1:
3 oz blackberries
2 tsp apple juice concentrate
1 tsp lemon juice
1/4 cup sour cherry juice
(natural foods store)
2 tbs protein powder
1/2 cup cottage cheese
2 tbs whipped cream

Wash and sort the blackberries. Set aside one blackberry for garnish. Put the remaining berries, apple juice concentrate, lemon juice, and cherry juice in a blender and blend thoroughly for 15 seconds. Press the fruit mixture through a fine sieve to remove the seeds.

Pour the fruit mixture back into the blender, and add the protein powder, and cottage cheese and blend vigorously for an additional ten seconds.

Place ice cubes in a large glass, pour the mixture over the top and garnish with whipped cream. Place the reserved blackberry on top. Serve the drink with a fat straw.

Blackberries

Blackberries supply loads of bioflavonoids, vitamins and minerals that keep you young, fortify your immune system, and arm your nerves against stress. These sweet, black, natural treasure chests contain, for example, carotenes, bioflavonoids, vitamin C, magnesium, and manganese.

Pineapple-
Lust for light
Kefir Drink

Remove the peel from the pineapple slice and set aside one piece of pineapple for garnish. Cut the remaining pineapple into small pieces, avoiding the core and put the fruit in a blender.
Squeeze the juice from the grapefruit and add the juice to the blender along with the sugar. Blend thoroughly.
Add the kefir and protein powder and blend at the lowest speed.
Place ice cubes in a tall glass and pour in the drink. Cut partway into the pineapple piece and place it on the rim of the glass. Serve the drink with a fat straw.

Serves 1:
1 thick slice of fresh pineapple
(about 4 oz with peel)
1/2 yellow grapefruit
2 tsp brown sugar
1/2 cup cold kefir
(natural foods store)
2 tbs protein powder

Pineapple

This exquisite tropical fruit is bursting with potassium, magnesium, phosphorus, iron, copper, zinc, manganese and iodine, all minerals that promote fat metabolism. The main contribution of pineapple to fitness is the enzyme bromelain, which aids in the digestion of protein. It guarantees that the important amino acids arrive at their place of effectiveness, your cells.
Weight-loss tip: Eat a slice of fresh pineapple before every meal.

power

Mango-
Carrot Mix

The drink of eternal youth, take two

Peel the mango. Cut away a nice mango wedge and set it aside for garnish. Coarsely chop the remaining mango and put it in a blender. Add the lime juice, honey, and half of the carrot juice and blend for fifteen seconds.

Add the remaining carrot juice, protein powder, and ginger and blend well for an additional ten seconds. Put ice cubes in a large glass and pour the mixture over the top. Place the mango wedge and carrot strips on the rim of the glass. Serve the drink with a straw.

Serves 1:
1 piece mango (about 4 oz)
1 tbs lime juice
2 tsp floral honey
2/3 cup cold carrot juice
2 tbs protein powder
2 pinches ground ginger
2 carrot strips (use a
vegetable peeler)

Mangos

This fruit seduces you with its unique flavor and incomparable provitamin A content. With 6000 I.U. of vitamin A, mangos beat out every other fruit and any vitamin pill. Only carrots can keep up—and the two together are an ideal combination. Antiaging vitamin A prevents cancer and blocks free radicals, the destructive substances that cause your cells to age faster. Take care: Don't drink milk or alcohol two hours before or after eating mangos to avoid upsetting your stomach.

Tomato-

A spicy revitalizer

Avocado Drink

Peel the avocado, dice the flesh, and put it in a blender. Drizzle with the lemon juice. Add half of the tomato juice and blend thoroughly for fifteen seconds.

Serves 1:
About 2 oz ripe avocado
2 tbs lemon juice
1/2 cup cold tomato juice
2 tbs protein powder
1/4 cup mineral water
Salt to taste
Pepper to taste
Several drops of Tabasco sauce
2 cherry tomatoes

Add the protein powder, the remaining tomato juice, and the mineral water. Season to taste with salt, pepper, and Tabasco. Blend vigorously for an additional ten seconds.

Put ice cubes in a glass and pour the mixture over the top. Wash the tomatoes, pat them dry, and use them to garnish the drink. Serve the drink with a straw.

Tomatoes

Doctors prescribe these "love apples" as an anticancer food (due to the lycopene), as a tonic for your heart and kidneys, and as a remedy for gout and rheumatism. Tomatoes are low in calories and their potassium content makes them a diuretic. They're rich in magnesium, calcium, iron, and zinc. Tomatoes' nutrients stimulate digestion, clean out your intestines, and keep you slim. And tomatoes improve your mood. A tomato drink in the morning makes you feel alive and optimistic and helps you deal with stress.

power

Spicy Vegetable Shake
Good mood mix

Serves 1:
2 oz red bell pepper
2-3 cherry tomatoes
2 oz celery root
3 sprigs fresh Italian parsley
1/2 cup cold spicy tomato juice
2 tbs protein powder
1/4 cup vegetable stock
Herb salt to taste
Black pepper to taste

Wash and trim the bell pepper and tomatoes. Peel the celery root. Set aside a nice piece of bell pepper and celery root, and one cherry tomato for garnish. Dice the remaining vegetables. Rinse the parsley, set aside a small sprig for garnish, remove the remaining leaves from the stalks, and chop the leaves coarsely.

Put the bell pepper, celery root, tomatoes, and parsley in a blender. Add the tomato juice and blend thoroughly for fifteen seconds. Add the protein powder and stock, and season with herb salt and pepper. Blend vigorously for an additional ten seconds. Pour the drink into a tall glass. Thread the reserved bell pepper and celery root pieces and the cherry tomato onto a cocktail skewer and lay them across the rim of the glass. Garnish with the reserved parsley.

Bell Peppers

Bell peppers are pure tonic. Their capsaicin and vitamin C fortify your immune system and their carotene (especially in red peppers) prevents cancer. Bell peppers aid digestion and circulation, work as a diuretic, ease pain, reduce stress, firm up connective tissue, improve concentration, and combat arthritis.

power

Icy Cucumber-
The fit and trim drink
Dill Drink

Dice the frozen cucumber and put it in a blender. Rinse the dill and set aside a nice sprig for garnish. Remove the remaining leaves from the stalks, chop the leaves coarsely, and add them to the blender along with the lemon juice, yogurt, and half of the kefir. Blend the contents thoroughly for fifteen seconds. Add the protein powder and the remaining kefir. Season with salt and pepper and blend thoroughly for an additional ten seconds.

Place ice cubes in a wide glass and pour the mixture over the top. Cut partway into the reserved cucumber slice and place it on the rim of the glass with the reserved dill. Serve the drink with a straw.

Serves 1:
1 piece frozen cucumber (about 3 oz, without peel or seeds)
3 small sprigs fresh dill
1 tsp lemon juice
1/4 cup plain low-fat yogurt
1/2 cup cold kefir (natural foods store)
2 tbs protein powder
Salt to taste
Black pepper to taste
1 slice cucumber

Cucumbers

With only thirteen calories per 4 ounces and an insulin-like hormone, cucumbers are true fat burners. For their magnesium and potassium, cucumbers have been dubbed the fruit of athletes. Their juice drives water out of your body, making it easier on your heart. Cucumbers' bitter constituents stimulate the liver and gallbladder. Doctors prescribe cucumbers for gout and rheumatism as well as for cleansing the skin. A slice of cucumber on your skin can smooth wrinkles, soothe minor rashes, and relieve eczema.

power

Green temptation

Carrot-
Herb Shake

Serves 1:
1 handful fresh chervil
3 sprigs fresh Italian parsley
1 tbs lemon juice
1 tsp floral honey
2 tbs ground hazelnuts
1/4 cup cold carrot juice
2 tbs protein powder
1/2 cup cold low-fat milk
Salt to taste
Black pepper to taste
1-2 drops Worcestershire sauce
A couple drops of olive oil
1 carrot stick

Wash the herbs and shake them dry. Set aside a small sprig of chervil for garnish. Remove the remaining chervil and parsley leaves from their stalks and chop the leaves finely. Put the herbs in a blender along with the lemon juice, honey, hazelnuts, and carrot juice. Blend vigorously for fifteen seconds.

Add the protein powder and milk. Season with salt, pepper, Worcestershire sauce, and olive oil. Blend for an additional ten seconds.

Pour the drink into a tall glass. Lay the carrot stick across the rim of the glass and garnish the drink with the reserved chervil.

► Carrots

Due to their high pectin content (a fiber that promotes healthy intestines) and skin-protecting vitamin A, carrots are an essential ingredient in fitness cocktails. Tip: Always consume them with a little olive oil so that their vitamin A can be easily transported to your cells.

Beet Cream

Contributes to a long life

Serves 1:
4-5 radishes (about 2 oz)
2 tbs low-fat plain yogurt
1/4 cup beet juice
2 tsp lemon juice
1/2 tsp grated horseradish
2 tbs protein powder
1/2 cup cold buttermilk
Salt to taste
Black pepper to taste
1 tsp chopped fresh chives

Wash and trim the radishes. Cut two nice slices from the radishes and set them aside for garnish. Chop the remaining radishes and put them in a blender along with the yogurt, beet juice, lemon juice, and horseradish. Blend well for fifteen seconds.

Add the protein powder and buttermilk. Season generously with salt and pepper and blend thoroughly for an additional ten seconds.

Pour the mixture into a large glass. Cut partway into the radish slices and place them on the rim of the glass. Sprinkle with the chives. Serve the drink with a fat straw.

Beets

These antiaging vegetables provide two fountains of youth: Folic acid and silicium. Folic acid protects blood vessels and the heart and participates in the production of hormones such as dopamine and norepinephrine that promote good moods, creativity, and power. Silicium is the trace element for beauty. It fortifies connective tissue and gives you firm skin, shiny hair, and hard nails. In addition, beets detoxify your body, work as a diuretic, and promote cell growth and the formation of red blood cells.

power

Celery Root

The anti-stress shake

Spinach Flip

Peel the celery root and set aside a narrow wedge for garnish. Grate the remaining celery root. Wash the spinach thoroughly, trim it, and chop it coarsely. Rinse the parsley and set aside a small sprig for garnish. Remove the remaining parsley leaves from the stalks and chop the leaves. Put the celery root, spinach, and parsley in a blender. Add the egg yolk, if using, lemon juice, and celery juice. Blend well for fifteen seconds. Add the protein powder and milk. Season with salt, pepper, and nutmeg and blend thoroughly for an additional ten seconds.

Pour the mixture into a tall glass. Cut partway into the celery root wedge and place it on the rim of the glass. Grind a little pepper over the top and garnish with the reserved parsley. Serve with a straw.

Serves 1:
2 oz celery root
1 oz tender spinach leaves
3 sprigs fresh Italian parsley
1 egg yolk (optional)
2 tsp lemon juice
1/4 cup celery juice (natural foods store)
2 tbs protein powder
1/2 cup cold low-fat milk
Salt to taste
Black pepper to taste
1 pinch freshly ground nutmeg

Celery Root

This vegetable lowers stress-related high blood pressure. In Asia, celery root has been used for 2000 years as a blood pressure-reducing remedy. The active substance 3-N-butyl phthalide reduces the stress hormones in the blood that constrict blood vessels. Certainly Hippocrates wasn't yet aware of this, but he still recommended celery root for everyone "whose nerves flutter."

power

Tutti-Frutti
Cocktail

Nature's energy drink

Wash and trim or peel the fruit. Set aside several pieces for garnish. Cut
the remaining fruit into small pieces and put them in a blender along
with the lemon juice, fructose, cottage cheese, and
half of the low-fat milk. Blend thoroughly for
fifteen seconds.

Add the protein powder, oat flakes, and the remaining
milk and blend well for an additional ten seconds.
Put ice cubes in a large glass and pour the mixture
over the top. Thread the reserved fruit onto a small
cocktail skewer and lay it across the rim of the glass.
Serve the drink with a fat straw.

Serves 1:
4 oz mixed fruit (e.g.,
strawberries, green grapes,
blackberries, bananas)
2 tsp lemon juice
1 tbs liquid fructose
(natural foods store)
2 tbs low-fat cottage cheese
1/2 cup cold low-fat milk
3 tbs protein powder
2 tbs instant oatmeal

Grapes

Grapes contain boron, which strengthens bones and
helps prevent osteoporosis. Their B vitamins steady
your nerves, their folic acid stimulates blood production, their vitamin C feeds your immune system,
their potassium lowers your blood pressure, and
their magnesium fortifies your muscles and heart.
Grapes keep your intestines and kidneys functioning
and promote better concentration.

power

Mocha-Banana

With stimulating espresso

Dream

Put the espresso and sugar in a blender. Peel the banana, cut it into several pieces, and add them to the blender along with half of the milk. Blend thoroughly for ten seconds.

Serves 1:
1/4 cup cold espresso
1 tsp brown sugar
2 oz banana
2/3 cup cold low-fat milk
3 tbs protein powder
1 tbs instant espresso powder
1 tbs whipped cream

Add the protein powder and the remaining milk and blend vigorously for an additional ten seconds. Moisten the rim of a tall glass and dip it into the espresso powder. Place ice cubes in a tall glass and pour the mixture over the top. Garnish with the whipped cream and the remaining espresso powder. Serve the drink with a straw and a long-handled spoon.

Coffee

The components of coffee boost metabolisms and stimulate brain activity. Coffee drinkers read faster, have a better short-term memory, and have a 40 percent lower risk of gallstones than non-coffee drinkers. Caffeine not only expands minds but also expands constricted bronchial tubes (asthma). Researchers in Scotland found that heart disease is more common in people who don't drink coffee. A healthy dose: One to three cups per day.

power

Chocolate-
Gives feelings of love
Orange Shake

Gradually bring the milk to a boil. Chop the chocolate coarsely, add it to the milk, and melt it while stirring occasionally. Remove the chocolate milk from the heat, pour it into a heatproof measuring cup or pitcher, and refrigerate for thirty minutes.

Serves 1:
1 cup low-fat milk
2 oz unsweetened chocolate
1 tsp lemon juice
3 tbs protein powder
1 tsp vanilla extract
1 scoop orange sherbet
1/2 slice orange

Pour the cold chocolate milk into a blender. Add the lemon juice, protein powder, and vanilla extract and blend well for fifteen seconds.

Put the orange sherbet in a tall glass and pour the chocolate milk over the top. Cut partway into the orange slice and place it on the rim of the glass. Serve the drink with a long-handled spoon and a straw.

Vanilla

The black bean whose pulp lends desserts an incomparable flavor originated in Central America and is a member of the orchid family. The wives of Aztec rulers knew the effects of cocoa drinks seasoned with vanilla on their men. Vanilla stimulates the kidneys, fortifies the stomach, and promotes good digestion. Vanilla was once forbidden in cloisters.

power

Tangy
Sour power
Lime Shake

Wash the lime under hot water, dry it, and finely grate the zest. Cut the lime in half and squeeze the juice from both halves. Put the lime juice, lime zest, cream cheese, and cream in a blender. Add the sugar and half of the milk and blend vigorously for fifteen seconds.

Add the protein powder and the remaining milk and thoroughly blend for an additional ten seconds.

Pour the mixture into a large glass. Cut partway into the strawberry and place it on the rim of the glass. Garnish the drink with the lime zest strip and serve it with a fat straw.

Serves 1:
1 lime (or 1/2 lemon)
1/3 cup low-fat cream cheese
2 tbs cream
2 tsp brown sugar
1/2 cup cold low-fat milk
3 tbs protein powder
1 ripe firm strawberry
1 strip of lime zest

Lime

Although this "lemon of the tropics" has less vitamin C than its big sister the lemon, it provides other benefits. It is rich in potassium, calcium, phosphorus, and aromatic oils. And it cheers the organic heart because its rind is usually untreated, allowing you to grate it and use its healthy bitter constituents as a spice.

power

Raspberry-Poppy
Sweet, irresistible seduction
Seed Cream

In a saucepan, bring the milk and cream to a boil. Slit open the vanilla bean lengthwise, scrape out the pulp and add the bean and pulp to the milk. Sprinkle in two-thirds of the poppy seeds and simmer for five minutes over very low heat. Remove the vanilla bean.

Serves 1:
1/2 cup cold low-fat milk
2 tbs cream
1/2 vanilla bean
1 tbs poppy seeds
3 oz raspberries
1 tbs maple syrup
3 tsp lemon juice
3 tbs protein powder
1 lemon slice

Briefly rinse the raspberries and sort them. Set aside four nice berries for garnish. Put the remaining raspberries, maple syrup, two teaspoons of the lemon juice, and six tablespoons of the poppy seed milk in the blender and blend for fifteen seconds. Add the protein powder and the remaining poppy seed milk and blend for an additional ten seconds. Moisten the rim of a glass with the remaining lemon juice and dip it into the remaining poppy seeds. Pour the milk mixture into the glass. Thread the lemon slice and reserved raspberries onto a cocktail skewer and lay them across the rim of the glass. Serve the drink with a straw.

Raspberries

In France, raspberries are considered to be a medicinal plant. They spice up your health with potassium (to reduce blood pressure), iron (to promote blood production), and magnesium (to fortify heart and muscles). Their acids, pectin, and tannins aid the liver in detoxifying the body and even reduce fevers. Raspberries' biotin adds shine to your hair, their seeds stimulate digestion, and their carotenes protect your skin and sharpen your vision.

power

Fitness Food

Energy for
for more stamina, conditioning, and performance
Sport & Fitness

WHAT MAKES ATHLETES FIT

One thing is obvious: If you exercise several times a week, you need more energy than those who are sedentary. Regardless of whether you ride a bike, swim, hike, play tennis, or jog, you can and should eat more than if you were a couch potato. Yet that fact does not give you carte blanche to blindly fill up on anything you want with the excuse that it will be "worked off" while you exercise. On the contrary: only properly fed muscles will give you true power and an optimal workout.

CARBOHYDRATES, CARBOHYDRATES, AND MORE CARBOHYDRATES!

Carbohydrates are what give you strength and stamina. Eating them is like tanking up with super-premium-grade gasoline. Carbohydrates are also the best source of energy for nerves and the brain. Carbohydrates are converted into glycogen by your body and stored in your liver and muscles. Your muscles draw on this glycogen during a workout. Yet only about 240-500 grams of glycogen are stored in the liver and muscles. That is the equivalent to about 1,000 to 2,000 kcal. During high-performance activities and endurance sports, your body needs to draw on its reserves. Once the glycogen stores are depleted, the body draws on its protein stores, to the detriment of your muscle mass. Fat deposits are also drawn on for energy, but that does not result in as much power as the energy obtained from carbohydrates. A normal, balanced diet for most people consists of at most about 55 percent carbohydrates. The body requires two to three days to replenish glycogen stores depleted by a workout or competition. The more you increase the percentage of carbohydrates in your diet (to 60-70 percent), the faster you will regain that lost energy.

DRINK PLENTY OF WATER

You need to drink plenty of water on a regular basis; if you wait until you are thirsty, it's already too late. Your body can no longer adequately compensate for the loss of fluids, and your performance is compromised. You should drink at least 2 glasses of water before even beginning a workout. If your workout lasts longer than 45 minutes, you should drink fluids while you are working out as well. A mixture of apple juice and mineral water is a good option since the minerals and carbohydrates give you additional stamina.

THE LEGEND OF PROTEIN

A common adage is that athletes need more protein to build strength, but that is not the case. Only athletes participating in strength sports, such as weight-lifting, need more protein in accordance with their higher body weight.

An excess of unused protein is converted into fat and ends up as fat deposits in undesirable locations. You do not need to buy expensive products from a drugstore or health food store to find high-quality sources of protein. You can find such sources in common foods, such as potatoes with an egg and cheese, or legumes with grains.

FAT, BUT NOT TOO MUCH FAT

Athletes should ideally consume a low-fat diet. Too much fat, especially from animal products, puts a strain on the body. Too little or no fat at all would be just as damaging. The following rule of thumb applies: fat should comprise only about 30 percent of your total day's calories.

Fat can consist of butter or margarine on your toast, high-quality olive oil on your salad, and fish two or three times a week. Cold water fish, such as salmon, herring, or mackerel, contain the omega-3 fatty acids so important for your body.

The Right Thing

Nutritious snacks for optimal performance

at the Right Time

TO START OFF YOUR DAY

Always eat breakfast, regardless of whether you plan to work out on a given day. Breakfast is essential for giving you that extra edge needed by more than just your muscles—your brain profits as well. Without breakfast, your glycogen stores are half-empty and continue to drain throughout the morning. A midday low is preprogrammed. So always kick off your day with a hearty portion of carbohydrates. This may mean that you have to change your habits a bit, but the 15 minutes you need for a quick meal in the morning will pay off and enhance your mood all day long.

BEFORE YOUR WORKOUT

Shortly before your workout, your glycogen stores should ideally be completely topped off. You can accomplish this by eating a small carbohydrate-rich, low-fiber snack. Bananas are an outstanding choice—the quintessential fruit for athletes. Less ideal choices are foods rich in fat or protein, as these meals are digested slowly and reduce your performance.

DURING A WORKOUT

If you work out for longer than 45 minutes at a time, you should always have fluids on hand. It is not a good idea to eat something since solids would put an additional strain on your body's digestion. The exception to this is, naturally, if you are taking an all-day hike or playing tennis for hours. But even in these cases a small snack, such as a granola or fruit bar or a piece of fruit, are sufficient to replenish your glycogen stores.

It is far more important that you drink fluids to replace the minerals you lose through perspiration. Your mineral water should contain at least 100 mg magnesium per quart. Fruit juices or fruit juice/mineral water mixtures are also good supplies of carbohydrates.

You should always avoid alcohol to quench your thirst. Although beer does contain many minerals and carbohydrates, the alcohol content impairs their absorption by the body, has a diuretic effect, and impairs the replenishment of glycogen stores.

ALWAYS EAT AFTER
A WORKOUT

After an intensive workout, you may not feel hungry for about an hour. Only after your metabolism and circulation return to normal will you feel hunger signals from your body. Yet your body is crying out for minerals and energy since it is considerably depleted from your efforts. The glycogen stores in your muscles are empty, and they need carbohydrates immediately, otherwise muscle cells will be broken down instead of being built up again. Starting on page 35, you will find meals ideal for replenishing your reserves.

After a workout your body is also weakened from the huge efforts it has expended. This leaves the playing field open to free radicals, making it particularly easy for them to start attacking the cells in your body. Antioxidant vitamins C and E are particularly helpful in preventing this from happening. Fruits, fresh vegetables, and fruit and vegetable juices are a great source of vitamin C. When you perspire, you lose valuable minerals as well as water—for some more, for others less. Magnesium and calcium are the minerals you lose in greatest quantities, which is why it is especially important that the snack you eat after a workout and any fluids you drink should contain these two minerals.

Ingredients
Power from natural sources
for Fitness

FOODS WITH IMPACT

Apricots: A source of B vitamins, carotenoids, potassium, and silicic acids, these small fruits are packed full of fitness-enhancing ingredients. In the winter months, dried unsulfured apricots are a good substitute for fresh.

Bananas: Here's a fruit custom-made for athletes. Bananas are full of magnesium, potassium, beta carotene, biotin, and vitamin C, and they also contain just the right amount of carbohydrates for a boost in stamina.

Beets: In addition to magnesium and potassium, beets also contain the blood-fortifying mineral iron. You can prepare them in a variety of ways and they can also be cooked in advance.

Carrots: Whether nibbled on, consumed as juice, or grated in a salad, carrots are packed with energy and are easy to take along as snacks.

Currants: A source of B vitamins, beta carotene, and vitamin C, currents are a great aid in achieving overall fitness.

Dried Fruits: Good sources of all minerals, dried fruits are an essential component of fitness nutrition. They're a better choice for nibbling than chocolate or cookies.

Fish: You should eat fish two to three times a week. Fish is a particularly valuable source of polyunsaturated fatty acids.

Legumes: Athletes can't miss with beans and lentils, which contain vitamins, minerals, and are a highly nutritious source of pure protein.

Oatmeal or Oat Bran: A good source of vitamins B1 and E as well as the minerals, calcium and magnesium, even small amounts of oat products provide sufficient carbohydrates.

Seed Oils: These are a good source of omega-6 fatty acids, also known as linoleic acids. Polyunsaturated fatty acids are essential to life. Eat 1-2 tablespoons per day.

Seeds and Nuts: These are a good source of magnesium, potassium, and an extra dose of vitamin E. Try sprinkling them over a salad or into your morning cereal.

Rice and Wild Rice: These are outstanding sources of carbohydrates and minerals.

Whole-Grain Products: These are mandatory for people active in sports, if only due to the complex carbohydrates they offer. They also supply all minerals and nearly all vitamins.

Substance	Needed for	Important sources	Daily requirements*
Magnesium	Muscle activity, nerves, enzymes, cell energy, hormone transportation, immune system, mineral utilization, heart function	Mineral water, whole grain products, legumes, potatoes, green vegetables, milk products	300-350 mg
Potassium	Nerve impulses, cell metabolism, enzymes, supply of oxygen to the brain, fluid balance, carbohydrate metabolism, heart beat	Fruit, dried fruits, potatoes	3-4 g
Vitamin E (Tocopherol)	Enzyme reactions, nerves, muscles, skin, circulation, fat metabolism, protects cells from free radicals	Vegetable oils, particularly seed oils, peas, nuts, avocado	12 mg
Vitamin B1 (Thiamin)	Processing of carbohydrates, transmission of nerve stimuli, activation of magnesium	Legumes, whole-grain bread, potatoes, poultry, liver	1.1-1.5 mg
Vitamin B2 (Riboflavin)	Protein and carbohydrate metabolism, skin	Milk products, meat, fish, eggs, whole-grain bread	1.8 mg
Vitamin B12 (Cobalamin)	Formation of red blood cells (together with iron), activates enzymes for provision of muscle energy	Liver, salmon, eggs, milk products	5 mcg = .005 mg
Niacin	Enzyme for energy transfer, heart and nervous system	Whole-grain bread, beef, poultry, salmon, yeast	15-20 mg
Biotin (Vitamin H)	Synthesis of carbohydrates and fatty acids, energy supply, nervous system, skin, hair, nails	Organ meats, milk, soy beans, whole-grain bread, lentils, chicken liver	0.03-0.1 mg
Vitamin C (Ascorbic acid)	Iron utilization, immune system, blood formation, blood vessels	Bell peppers, tomatoes, cauliflower, citrus fruits, currants	75 mg
Beta carotene	Immune system	Orange-colored fruits and vegetables, green vegetables, tomatoes	need info
Iron	Transportation of oxygen in the blood, muscle tissues, heart function, hormone metabolism	Beef with salad or vegetables, lentils with vegetables, whole-grain bread with fruit	10-15 mg

* The daily requirements of magnesium, potassium, vitamin E and vitamin C may double for those participating in intense sports activities.

Power
Vitamins and minerals you can enjoy
Week

EVERYDAY FITNESS

Our weekly eating plan gives you a sample meal plan for days on which you exercise. But feel free to enjoy these meals every day of the week—they are low in fat and high in flavor. On the days you don't work out, simply enjoy the before- and after-workout snacks whenever you like, or replace them with a piece of fruit.

PLENTY OF CARBOHYDRATES

We have designed each day so you consume approximately 200 g of pure carbohydrates. Depending on your training regimen, you can increase your carbohydrates on particularly intense days by adding bananas, more rice, or a larger portion of bread.

PLENTY OF MAGNESIUM

Athletes cannot meet their daily magnesium requirements through solid food alone. That's why it's particularly important that you make sure your mineral water is a good source of magnesium (at least 100 mg per quart—just look on the label).

FITNESS YOU CAN DRINK

The drinks in our recipe section are powerhouses of nutrition! You can drink them throughout the day or before a workout. They do not have enough carbohydrates to serve as a meal after a workout, though.

PURE NATURE INSTEAD OF BOTTLED CONCOCTIONS

You could obviously also get the vitamins and minerals you need from the drugstore. But be aware that your body can absorb and use these nutrients much more efficiently when they are delivered in small amounts throughout the day instead of just one large dose once a day. In addition, vitamins and minerals can have beneficial effects when consumed together. For example, the body can absorb magnesium even better when it is consumed together with the water-soluble vitamin B1. If you plan your meals carefully, your body can receive everything it needs.

WEEKLY PLAN

Monday

* Breakfast: Rice Flakes with Peaches * Before: 2 Herbed Muffins with Ham
* After: Dried Fruit Pancakes * Herb-Encrusted Pike-Perch
* Beverage: Deep Purple Power Drink

Tuesday

* Breakfast: Avocado Cream on Whole-Grain Bread * Before: 2 Corn Flake Muffins
* After: White Bean Salad with Celery * Turkey Breast in Coconut Milk
* Beverage: Yogurt Shake with Mango and Orange

Wednesday

* Breakfast: Shrimp on Pumpernickel * Before: 2 Banana Muffins with Hazelnuts
* After: Prosciutto with Mushrooms* Beef Fillets with Zucchini and Spaghetti
* Beverage: Sweet Apricot Cooler

Thursday

* Breakfast: Banana-Melon Salad * Before: Yogurt Shake with Mango and Orange
* After: Tuna Cream on Whole-Grain Toast * Pork Tenderloin in Persimmon Sauce
* Beverage: Tropical Shake

Friday

* Breakfast: Orange-Almond Muesli with Figs* Before: Bean Spread with Leeks
* After: Mango-Currant Salad * Apricot-Chicken Ragout
* Beverage: Hot Pepper Milk

Saturday

* Breakfast: Prosciutto with Cottage Cheese * Before: Cheese and Cucumber
Sandwich * After: Couscous Salad with Corn and Sage * Swordfish-Mango Ragout
* Beverage: Melon-Currant Froth

Sunday

* Breakfast: Mango Muesli * Before: Melon Puree with Figs
* After: Fennel-Pineapple Salad * Leek-Wrapped Salmon Fillets
* Beverage: Vegetable Cooler

Shrimp on

rich in vitamins and minerals

Pumpernickel

Serves 2: 2 oz low-fat cream cheese, softened • 1/4 cup low-fat plain yogurt • Salt to taste • Black pepper to taste • 4 slices pumpernickel bread • 2 tbs minced fresh chives, plus more for garnish • 1 carambola (star fruit) • 4 oz cooked and peeled shrimp

Stir together the cream cheese, yogurt, salt, and pepper. Use half of the cream cheese mixture to cover 2 slices of the bread, then sprinkle with the 2 tbs chives. Top each slice with another slice of bread and then spread with the remaining cream cheese mixture.

Cut the carambola in half crosswise, then cut off two star-shaped slices, and set aside. Dice the remaining carambola, then toss with the shrimp. Divide the shrimp mixture among the tops of the sandwiches. Garnish with the carambola stars and remaining chives and serve.

PER SERVING: 315 calories • 22 g protein • 8 g fat • 38 g carbohydrates

Mango
rich in vitamin E, potassium, and magnesium
Muesli

Serves 2: 1/4 cup low-fat milk • 1/3 cup whole-grain cereal flakes • 1 tbs crème fraîche • 2 tbs sunflower kernels • 1 fresh mango

In a bowl, pour the milk over the rye flakes, then stir in the crème fraîche and let stand for 10 minutes. Toast the sunflower kernels in a dry nonstick skillet. Peel the mango, cut the fruit from the hard pit, dice the flesh, and fold it into the flakes. Sprinkle with toasted sunflower kernels and serve.

PER SERVING: 257 calories • 7 g protein • 10 g fat • 34 g carbohydrates

Orange-Almond
rich in magnesium and potassium
Muesli with Figs

Serves 2: About 2 oz dried figs • 3 tbs whole-grain oatmeal • 1/4 cup low-fat milk • 1 orange • 1/4 cup slivered almonds • 2/3 cup low-fat plain yogurt • Pinch of ground cinnamon

Finely chop the figs, then combine with oatmeal and milk in a bowl, and let stand for 5 minutes. Peel and dice the orange. Toast the slivered almonds in a dry nonstick skillet. Fold the diced oranges and yogurt into the muesli. Sprinkle with the toasted almonds and cinnamon before serving.

PER SERVING: 262 calories • 10 g protein • 10 g fat • 36 g carbohydrates

Rice Flakes
rich in carbohydrates and magnesium
with Peaches

Serves 2: 1 1/4 cups low-fat milk • 2 tbs raw (turbinado) sugar • 1 cup rice flakes (health food store) • 3 fresh peaches (about 10 oz) • 1 tbs pistachio nuts • 2 tbs raisins • 2 tbs corn flakes

Heat the milk and the sugar, stirring to dissolve the sugar, until just under the boiling point. Pour the mixture over the rice flakes, cover, and let stand for 10 minutes. Briefly plunge the peaches into boiling water, then remove the peels with a sharp knife. Dice the peach flesh, removing the pits. Chop the pistachio nuts and toast them in a dry nonstick skillet. Gently fold the diced peaches and raisins into the rice flakes. Sprinkle with the corn flakes and pistachios and serve.

PER SERVING: 384 calories • 8 g protein • 4 g fat • 80 g carbohydrates

Banana-Melon
for increased muscle performance
Salad

Serves 2: 2 bananas • 5 tbs oat bran • 2 tsp mango chutney • 1/2 cantaloupe or honeydew melon (about 10 oz fruit) • 2 tbs pine nuts

In a bowl, mash the bananas with a fork. Stir in the oat bran and mango chutney. Remove the seeds from the melon half and cut the melon into wedges. Remove the rind, then cut the melon flesh into pieces and stir into the banana mixture. Chop the pine nuts, toast them in a dry nonstick skillet, and sprinkle over the fruit.

PER SERVING: 275 calories • 5 g protein • 6 g fat • 53 g carbohydrates

Prosciutto with

with honeydew melon and tomato juice

Cottage Cheese

Serves 2:

1/4 honeydew melon (about 5 oz)

1/2 cup low-fat cottage cheese

Salt to taste

Black pepper to taste

2 whole-wheat rolls

About 2 oz prosciutto, sliced paper-thin

1 1/4 cups tomato juice

Remove the seeds from the melon, then slice the melon into wedges, and remove the rind. Cut the melon into very small cubes and place in a bowl.

Mix the cottage cheese with the diced melon and season with salt and pepper.

Cut the rolls in half and spread each half with the melon-cottage cheese mixture. Fold each prosciutto slice into a loose spiral and arrange on the rolls, dividing evenly. A glass of tomato juice rounds out the meal.

Tomato juice

A substance called lycopene gives tomatoes their bright red color. Lycopene benefits the body by slowing down the absorption of free radicals in the body. The best thing is that lycopene remains in tomato products, even after processing—in tomato juice, for instance. Heating actually aids in lycopene utilization.

Per Serving:

202 calories

19 g protein

4 g fat

24 g carbohydrates

Red Grapefruit
with Italian amaretti
and Prunes

Serves 2: 1 red grapefruit • 5 tbs wheat germ • 10 pitted prunes (about 2 oz) • 1 1/2 cups low-fat plain yogurt • 10 amaretti cookies

With a long sharp knife, carefully remove the peel from the grapefruit, taking care to remove the white pith. Cut between the fruit's membranes to remove the grapefruit "fillets;" make sure to remove the seeds and collect the juice that escapes. Mix the grapefruit fillets, juice, and wheat germ in a bowl. Cut the prunes into strips and fold them into the grapefruit/wheat germ mixture together with the yogurt. Spoon the mixture into bowls. Crush the amaretti, sprinkle among the bowls, and serve.

PER SERVING: 146 calories • 6 g protein • 2 g fat • 25 g carbohydrates

Camembert Spread
also good as a snack
with Rye Bread

Serves 2: About 2 oz ripe Camembert cheese • 4 oz low-fat cream cheese, softened • 1-2 tbs milk • Salt to taste • White pepper to taste • 1/2 tsp sweet paprika • 2 green onions • 4 slices rye bread • 2 tbs minced fresh chives

Cut the Camembert into small pieces, removing the rind. Mash the camembert, then mix it with the cream cheese and milk. Season with salt, pepper, and the paprika. Wash and trim the green onions, cut them in half lengthwise, and mince. Stir the minced green onions into the Camembert mixture and spread onto the slices of bread. Garnish with the chives.

PER SERVING: 398 calories • 18 g protein • 20 g fat • 37 g carbohydrates

Avocado Cream on
with strawberries and sprouts
Whole-Grain Bread

Cut the avocado in half and remove the pit. Using a spoon, scoop out the flesh of the avocado, place it in a bowl, and coarsely mash it with a fork. Mix in the salt, pepper, and raspberry vinegar. Lightly toast the bread, then spread the avocado mixture on the slices. Using kitchen scissors, cut the sprouts into pieces and sprinkle over the bread slices. Wash the strawberries and remove the stems, then cut the strawberries into slices. Distribute the strawberries over the bread slices, and season to taste with freshly ground pepper.

Serves 2:
1 small ripe avocado
Salt to taste
Black pepper to taste
2 tbs raspberry vinegar
4 slices whole-grain bread
1/2 box alfalfa sprouts
4 fresh strawberries

Avocados

Avocados boast the highest natural fat content of all fruits and vegetables. Three quarters of the fat content consists of easily digested polyunsaturated fats. Avocados are also a rich source of biotin, which controls energy production in the muscles. In addition, biotin positively affects the protein metabolism of skin, hair, and nails, which is why avocados are also considered a "beauty fruit."

PER SERVING:

380 calories

11 g protein

19 g fat

49 g carbohydrates

Yogurt Shake with
a terrific source of magnesium and potassium
Mango and Orange

Finely chop the sunflower kernels, then toast in a dry nonstick skillet until their aroma is released; set aside to cool. Peel the mango and cut the flesh from the pit in wedges, taking care to catch any juice in a bowl. Set aside 2 mango wedges for garnish. Squeeze the juice from the orange and the lime half. Puree the remaining mango flesh with the orange and lime juices, oat bran, yogurt, and water in a blender or with a hand blender. Fill 2 glasses with the yogurt mixture and sprinkle with the toasted sunflower kernels. Garnish each glass with a wedge of mango and serve the drinks immediately.

Serves 2:

1 tbs sunflower kernels

1 ripe fresh mango

1 orange

1/2 lime

2 tbs oat bran

3/4 cup low-fat plain yogurt

1/4 cup water

Mangos—A favorite through the ages

Mangos are believed to have been cultivated in India over 6,000 years ago and are a symbol of strength and power. That's not surprising, since they are a rich source of beta carotene, vitamins, and minerals. Fresh mangos can now be found nearly everywhere and can be served in a variety of ways—even as a side dish for meat or fish.

PER SERVING:

197 calories

7 g protein

4 g fat

38 g carbohydrates

Deep Purple
Power Drink
with beets for peak energy

Serves 2: 2 fresh beets (about 7 oz each) • 2 small tart apples • 2 medium carrots • Juice from 1/2 lemon • 2 tsp prepared horseradish • Celery salt to taste • White pepper to taste

Wash and peel the beets, then cut into eighths (wear gloves to prevent your hands from becoming discolored). Wash, quarter, and core the apples. Wash the carrots. Run the beets, apples, and carrots through a juicer. Mix the resulting juice with the lemon juice and horseradish. Season to taste with the celery salt and pepper.

PER SERVING: 92 calories • 2 g protein • 1 g fat • 21 g carbohydrates

Sweet Apricot
rich in potassium for top performance
Cooler

Serves 2: 18 oz ripe fresh apricots • 1 lime • 2 red grapefruits • 1 tbs raw (turbinado) sugar • Mineral water • 2 leaves fresh mint

Wash, pit, and run the apricots through a juicer. Cut the lime and grapefruits in half. Press the juice from one lime half and all of the grapefruits. Moisten the rims of the glasses with water and dip them in the sugar. Mix the apricot, grapefruit and lime juices, pour into the glasses, then top off with mineral water. Cut the remaining lime half in half again. Garnish the drinks with quarters of lime and mint leaves.

PER SERVING: 140 calories • 3 g protein • 1 g fat • 30 g carbohydrates

Green Pick-
for instant energy
Me-Up

Serves 2: 7 oz cucumbers • 2 kiwis • 3 sprigs fresh dill • 1 cup buttermilk • 1/2 tsp ground cumin • Salt to taste • Black pepper to taste • Cold mineral water

Peel the cucumbers and the kiwis. Wash the dill, shake dry, and remove the leaves from the stem. Puree the cucumbers, kiwis, buttermilk, and dill. Season the drink with the cumin, salt, and pepper. Let the mixture stand for several minutes before filling the glasses and topping off with cold mineral water.

PER SERVING: 116 calories • 6 g protein • 2 g fat • 21 g carbohydrates

Tropical
rich in magnesium and calcium
Shake

Serves 2: 1 fresh pineapple (about 10 oz) • 1 banana • 5 sprigs fresh mint • 1 cup buttermilk • 2 tbs maple syrup • 1 tbs sesame seeds

Remove the pineapple rind, then cut the pineapple into quarters lengthwise, and remove the hard inner core. Cut the pineapple into pieces. Peel the banana. Remove the mint leaves from the stems and set aside several leaves. Puree the pineapple, banana, mint leaves, and buttermilk. Mix in the maple syrup and sesame seeds. Mince the remaining mint leaves. Serve the drink in glasses garnished with mint.

PER SERVING: 188 calories • 2 g protein • 2 g fat • 43 g carbohydrates

Melon-Currant

very high in minerals

Froth

Serves 2:

4 oz fresh red currants
1/2 honeydew melon
1 tsp wildflower honey
1/2 cup buttermilk
2 tsp sugar

Wash the currants and set aside two sprigs for garnish; remove the remaining currants from the stems. Cut the melon in half and scoop out the seeds. Cut one melon half into wedges and remove the rind, then cut the fruit into 1/2-inch cubes. Puree the currants, melon, honey, and buttermilk in a blender or with a hand blender. Moisten the rims of 2 glasses with water and dip them into the sugar. Divide the drink among the glasses, garnish each with a sprig of currants, and serve immediately.

> ## Currants—An energy powerhouse

Red currants are an outstanding source of beta carotene, B vitamins, and vitamin C. On top of that, they are packed with potassium and calcium. These small berries are an energy powerhouse and are delicious any way you look at them—whether eaten as a snack or combined with buttermilk, yogurt, or kefir. Fresh currants can be hard to find, but they're worth searching for. Look for them in organic foods' stores during the summer months.

PER SERVING:

157 calories

4 g protein

1 g fat

33 g carbohydrates

Hot Pepper
for fans of spicy drinks
Milk

Serves 2: 2 tbs sesame seeds • 2 red bell peppers • 4 vine-ripened tomatoes • Salt to taste • Black pepper to taste • Dash Tabasco sauce • 1 1/4 cups ice-cold low-fat milk

Toast the sesame seeds in a dry nonstick skillet until they are golden brown, then set aside. Cut the bell peppers in half, wash, and remove the stems, seeds, and ribs. Wash the tomatoes, then cut in half, and remove the stems. Run the tomatoes and bell peppers through a juicer. Season the juice with salt, pepper, and Tabasco sauce. Pour the juice into glasses, top off with milk, and garnish with the toasted sesame seeds.

84

PER SERVING: 128 calories • 6 g protein • 5 g fat • 17 g carbohydrates

Celery-Bell Pepper
for circulation and metabolism
Powerhouse

Serves 2: 2 yellow bell peppers • 1 lb celery • Dash of cayenne pepper • 1 tbs minced fresh basil • 1 tsp coarse salt • Mineral water • 2 leaves fresh basil

Cut the bell peppers in half, and remove the stem, seeds, and ribs. Juice the celery and the bell pepper, then season the juice with cayenne pepper. Mix the minced basil with the salt and spread the mixture out on a plate. Moisten the rims of the glasses with water and dip into the salt/basil mixture. Pour the juice into the glasses, top off with mineral water, and garnish with the basil leaves.

PER SERVING: 70 calories • 4 g protein • 1 g fat • 13 g carbohydrates

Vegetable Cooler

high in potassium and beta carotene

Serves 2: 1 papaya • 1/4 fresh pineapple • Juice from 1/2 lime • 1 cup cold low-fat milk • Mineral water • 1 tbs grated unsweetened coconut

Cut the papaya in half, remove the seeds, and scoop out the flesh with a spoon. Peel the pineapple, taking care to cut out any remaining brown spots. Slice off two thin sections and set aside, then cut the remaining pineapple into small pieces. Puree the pineapple with the papaya, lime juice, and milk. Top off with mineral water. Moisten the rims of the glasses and dip into the coconut. Serve garnished with pineapple slices.

PER SERVING: 161 calories • 3 g protein • 3 g fat • 31 g carbohydrates

Bell Pepper-Carrot Mix

a dash of oil promotes vitamin A absorption

Serves 2: 1 yellow bell pepper • 2 bulbs kohlrabi • 18 oz carrots • 2 tsp minced fresh Italian parsley • Celery salt to taste • 2 drops wheat germ oil

Cut the bell pepper in half, wash, and remove the stem, seeds and ribs. Peel the kohlrabi and carrots. Run the vegetables through a juicer. Stir the parsley and celery salt into the juice. Pour the juice into 2 glasses, stir 1 drop of oil into each glass, and serve immediately.

PER SERVING: 104 calories • 5 g protein • 1 g fat • 19 g carbohydrates

Herbed Muffins

a hearty snack for those on the go

with Ham

Preheat the oven to 400°F. Clean and finely dice the green onions. Cut about 2 oz of the ham into small cubes. Heat the oil in a nonstick skillet. Sauté the green onions and diced ham until the onions are translucent, then set aside.

Put the cream cheese, milk, egg, salt, pepper, and cheese in a bowl and mix well. In another bowl, mix the flour, sugar, and baking powder. Add the flour mixture to the cream cheese mixture and stir just until blended, adding a little more milk if necessary. Fold in the green onion/ham mixture, parsley, and thyme.

Lightly oil the muffin pans, then spoon in the batter. Cut the remaining 1 oz ham into strips and arrange in a crisscross pattern over the tops of the muffins. Bake the muffins in the middle of the preheated oven for about 20–25 minutes, until they are golden brown. Let the muffins stand on a rack until cool.

Makes 12 muffins:

2 green onions

About 3 oz lean cooked ham

2 tbs vegetable oil

5 oz low-fat cream cheese, softened

3-5 tbs milk

1 egg

Salt to taste

Black pepper to taste

2 tbs freshly grated Gouda cheese

1 1/3 cups rye flour

1/2 tsp sugar

2 tsp baking powder

3 tbs minced fresh Italian parsley

1 tbs minced fresh thyme

Oil for the muffin pans

Good things come in small packages

Muffins—whether simple or sophisticated, sweet or spicy, as a snack or to go—are always well received. They taste best when they are fresh and still slightly warm. Muffins can also be frozen and easily reheated.

PER SERVING:

111 calories

5 g protein

6 g fat

11 g carbohydrates

Melon Puree
rich in potassium and vitamin C
with Figs

Serves 2: 2 ripe black figs • Juice of 1/2 lime • 1 tbs raw (turbinado) sugar • 1/2 honeydew melon • 2 tbs mascarpone cheese • Fresh mint leaves for garnish

Dice the figs. Stir together the lime juice and sugar, add the diced figs, and marinate for 10 minutes. Scoop out the seeds from the melon half, remove the rind, cut the melon into pieces, then puree. Stir the mascarpone until creamy, then fold it into the melon puree. Fold in the diced figs and marinade, then refrigerate the mixture for 1 hour. Garnish with mint leaves and serve.

PER SERVING: 113 calories • 1 g protein • 3 g fat • 20 g carbohydrates

Rice Waffles
ultralight and refreshing
with Currants

Serves 2: About 3 oz fresh red currants • 1 tsp agave syrup (health food store) • 1 tbs cottage cheese • 2 tbs low-fat plain yogurt • Black pepper • 2 rice waffles • Fresh thyme leaves

Remove the currants from the stems and place in bowl. Crush them lightly with a fork and drizzle with the agave syrup. Blend the cottage cheese with the yogurt until smooth, then season with pepper. Fold in the currants, then spoon the mixture onto the rice waffles and garnish with the thyme leaves.

PER SERVING: 119 calories • 1 g protein • 1 g fat • 26 g carbohydrates

Banana Muffins
bursting with carbohydrates for immediate energy
with Hazelnuts

Preheat the oven to 400° F. Use a hand mixer to blend the honey, margarine, and eggs in a bowl for 5 minutes until light and foamy. Peel and mash the bananas. Add the mashed bananas, hazelnuts, sugar, and vanilla and mix for another 2 minutes until lightly creamy. Mix together the flour and baking powder, then sift the flour into the mixture and stir in thoroughly.

Lightly oil the muffin pans and spoon in the batter. Take care to fill the pans to only two-thirds capacity, since the batter will rise during baking. Sprinkle the tops of the muffins with the raisins. Bake the muffins in the middle of the preheated oven for about 20 minutes, until golden brown. Let cool for a while in the pans and lightly brush muffins with maple syrup.

Makes 12:

1/4 cup honey

4 oz low-fat margarine

2 eggs

2 bananas

About 2 oz hazelnuts, ground

1 tbs sugar

1 tsp vanilla extract

1 1/2 cups whole wheat flour

2 tsp baking powder

Oil for the muffin pans

About 1/4 cup raisins

2 tbs maple syrup

Bananas

Bananas are the ideal fruit for athletes. Whether included in a recipe or simply eaten plain after a workout, bananas give you the carbohydrate kick you need. A great source of potassium and magnesium, bananas can help replenish your mineral stores. And bananas' high niacin content promotes improved energy acquisition.

PER SERVING:

193 calories

4 g protein

8 g fat

26 g carbohydrates

Corn Flake

a portable source of magnesium

Muffins

Preheat the oven to 400°F. Cut the apricots into thin strips. Trim, peel, and grate the carrots. Mix the grated carrot with the eggs and honey. Stir in the raisins, apricots, almonds, and orange zest.

Makes 12:
8 dried apricots
2 medium carrots
2 eggs
1/4 cup honey
2 tbs raisins
1/2 cup chopped almonds
Grated zest from 1/2 orange
1 cup whole wheat flour
2 tsp baking powder
Oil for the muffin pans
2 tbs apricot jam
2 tbs water
1/3 cup corn flakes

Mix together the flour and baking powder in a bowl. Sift the flour mixture into the wet ingredients and stir until a stiff batter is formed.

Lightly brush the muffin tin with oil. Divide the batter among the muffin cups and smooth the tops. Bake in the middle of the preheated oven for about 20 minutes, until golden brown. While the muffins are baking, put the apricot jam and water in a small pot and warm slowly until it becomes fluid. Once the muffins have finished baking, let them cool slightly on a rack. Brush the muffins with the apricot jam mixture, then sprinkle the corn flakes over the muffins and press down slightly so they adhere.

PER SERVING: 131 calories • 4 g protein • 4 g fat • 21 g carbohydrates

Bean Spread

also good as an appetizer

with Leeks

Serves 3–4:
1 small leek
1 medium carrot
1 tbs olive oil
1/2 cup vegetable stock
1 small can kidney beans (8.75 oz)
2 tbs minced fresh thyme
2 tsp capers (drained)
Salt to taste
Black pepper to taste

Trim the leek and the carrot. Cut the leek in half lengthwise, wash, then slice crosswise into half rings. Peel the carrot and cut into slices. Heat the olive oil in a nonstick skillet. Lightly sauté the vegetables in the oil over low heat, stirring constantly. Add the vegetable stock and cook over low heat for about 10-15 minutes, until the stock has evaporated and the vegetables are tender-crisp.

Drain the kidney beans, then puree the beans with the thyme, capers, leek, and carrot. Season the mixture with salt and pepper, then refrigerate.

This bean mixture makes a tasty dip for raw vegetables, but also works well as a spread for whole-grain bread. It keeps well for up to a week in the refrigerator.

Whole grains and legumes

The combination of whole grains and legumes is of particular biological value. Combined in this fashion, the protein in legumes can be ideally absorbed by the body. If you prefer to cut down on your consumption of animal-based protein, you can easily obtain the protein you need by pairing whole grains and legumes. Note: It's best to consult your doctor before beginning any new eating plan.

PER SERVING:

100 calories

5 g protein

3 g fat

13 g carbohydrates

Cheese and
replenishes carbohydrate stores
Cucumber Sandwich

Spread the cottage cheese on the bread slices. Wash and peel the cucumber, then cut into thin slices. Distribute the cucumber slices over the cottage cheese. Use a sharp knife to cut the Parmesan cheese into four thin slices. Arrange the cheese slices over the cucumbers.

Trim and wash the green onions, then slice into rings. Mix the chives and green onions with the salt, pepper, and vinegar. Stir in the oil.

Spoon the green onion mixture over the open-faced cheese sandwiches, then season to taste with freshly ground pepper.

Serves 2:
2 tbs cottage cheese
2 thick slices rye bread
4 oz cucumber
2 oz best-quality Parmesan cheese
2 green onions
2 tbs minced fresh chives
Salt to taste
Freshly ground pepper to taste
2 tbs white wine vinegar
2 tsp wheat germ oil

Variety—the spice of life
If you like, make the sandwich with different types of cheese. Depending on your preference, you can also use parsley or other fresh herbs instead of chives.

PER SERVING:
280 calories
17 g protein
14 g fat
21 g carbohydrates

Dried Fruit
with apricots and pineapple
Pancakes

Cut the apricots into small cubes. Coarsely chop the pineapple, then mix with the diced apricots. Put the fruit in a bowl, add the 1/2 cup milk, and let stand about 5 minutes. Remove the pineapple and set aside.

Beat the egg in a bowl, then stir in the milk-apricot mixture. Sift the flour, then gradually stir it into the egg mixture. Let the batter stand for about 2-3 minutes.

Heat 1 tsp butter in a small nonstick skillet (about 8 inches in diameter) and then fry two pancakes, one at a time, over high heat until golden brown. Spread 1 tsp sour cream over each pancake, then roll up the pancake, arrange as desired, and sprinkle with the pineapple. Serve each pancake with a glass of cold milk.

Serves 2:

1 oz dried apricots (unsulfured)
1 oz dried pineapple
1/2 cup low-fat milk, plus more for serving
1 egg
3-4 tbs whole wheat flour
2 tsp butter
2 tsp sour cream

Dried fruit powerhouses

Four ounces of dried figs contain 70 mg of magnesium and are an excellent source of potassium. That's why figs—as well as other dried fruits—are strongly recommended as a part of an athlete's diet. Other outstanding choices include dried apricots and plums, pineapple, and banana chips.

PER SERVING:

256 calories

9 g protein

9 g fat

34 g carbohydrates

Couscous Salad with

replenishes depleted magnesium levels

Corn and Sage

Serves 2: 2/3 cup water • 1/2 cup instant couscous • 2 tsp extra-virgin olive oil • 1 small can corn kernels (8.75 oz) • 4 oz mushrooms • 4 leaves fresh sage • 1/4 cup low-fat plain yogurt • 2 tbs white balsamic vinegar • Salt to taste • Black pepper to taste

Bring the water to a boil and add the couscous, then stir in the oil and let the couscous stand for 10 minutes. Drain the corn. Clean the mushrooms and cut into thin slices. Cut the sage into strips and mix everything with the couscous. Combine the yogurt with the vinegar, salt, and pepper, and stir into the salad.

PER SERVING: 369 calories • 12 g protein • 6 g fat • 68 g carbohydrates

Mango-Currant

also tasty with fresh peaches

Salad

Serves 2: 1 fresh mango • 4 fresh apricots • 4 oz fresh red currants • Juice from 1/2 lemon • 1 1/2 tbs raw (turbinado) sugar • 2 tbs water • 2 tbs rolled oats

Peel the mango, cut the flesh away from the pit, and cut the flesh into small cubes. Wash the apricots, then cut them in half, remove the pits, and cut into thin wedges. Wash the currants and remove them from the stems. Mix the mango cubes, apricots, and currants together. Sprinkle with lemon juice and arrange on plates. Melt the sugar in a pan with the water. Add the oatmeal and heat, stirring constantly, until lightly browned. Add the caramelized oats to the fruit salad.

PER SERVING: 240 calories • 3 g protein • 2 g fat • 51 g carbohydrates

Endive Salad
replenishes potassium and magnesium
with Apricots

Briefly plunge the apricots into boiling water, then remove the peels with a sharp knife. Cut the apricots in half, remove the pits, and cut the flesh into thin wedges. Coarsely chop the pumpkin seeds, toast them in a dry nonstick skillet, and set aside to cool.

In a bowl, mix together the maple syrup and vinegar and season to taste with salt and pepper. Gradually beat in the oil with a whisk. Add the apricot wedges and pumpkin seeds to the mixture and let stand for about 10 minutes.

Remove the outer leaves of the endive, then cut the heads in half lengthwise, and remove the cores. Cut the halves into strips between 1/4- and 1/2-inch wide, and mix well with the apricots. Arrange the salad on plates and serve.

Serves 2:

10 fresh apricots (about 12 oz)

1 tbs pumpkin seeds

1 tbs maple syrup

2 tbs balsamic vinegar

Salt to taste

Black pepper to taste

2 tbs pumpkin seed oil

2 small heads Belgian endive

Pumpkin seed oil

Pumpkin seed oil is derived from roasted pumpkin seeds. It is very dark in color and should be used sparingly. Take care when using this oil as it stains fabrics easily.

PER SERVING:

223 calories

5 g protein

11 g fat

25 g carbohydrates

White Bean Salad
a wonderful source of magnesium
with Celery

Drain the beans, rinse them with cold water, and let them drain again well. Trim and wash the green onions, and peel the garlic. Finely chop the green onions, and slice the garlic.

Serves 2:

3/4 can white beans (15-oz can)

2 green onions

2 cloves garlic

1 tbs olive oil

5 tbs raspberry vinegar

Salt to taste

Black pepper to taste

5 cherry tomatoes

1 stalk celery

2-4 tbs shelled walnuts

2 slices whole-grain bread

For the dressing, heat the oil in a small nonstick skillet. Add the green onions and garlic and sauté over medium heat until golden brown. Remove the pan from the heat and pour in the vinegar. Season the dressing with salt and pepper. While still warm, mix the dressing with the beans in a bowl.

Wash the cherry tomatoes, cut in half, and remove the stems. Peel and dice the celery. Mix the tomatoes and diced celery into the beans. Chop the walnuts. Arrange the salad on serving plates, sprinkle with walnuts, and accompany with the bread.

Beans

Red or white, dried or canned—in terms of nutrition for fitness buffs, beans should be in the picture frequently. One advantage: 3 1/2 oz of dried beans contain 341 mg of potassium and 39 mg of magnesium, and a high percentage of carbohydrates. Canned beans offer only slightly fewer nutrients than dried.

PER SERVING:

334 calories

13 g protein

13 g fat

39 g carbohydrates

Prosciutto with
also makes an elegant appetizer
Mushrooms

Serves 2: About 2 oz mushrooms • 1 tsp fresh lemon juice • About 2 oz prosciutto, thinly sliced • 1/4 cup mascarpone cheese • 2 tbs minced fresh chives • 2 thick slices dark bread • Freshly ground black pepper to taste

Clean the mushrooms, dice them finely, and sprinkle with the lemon juice. Remove any excess fat from the prosciutto, cut the meat into small pieces, and mix it with the mushrooms. Fold in the mascarpone and minced chives. Spread the mixture onto the bread slices, garnish with fresh-ground pepper, and serve.

Per Serving: 194 calories • 11 g protein • 10 g fat • 15 g carbohydrates

Tuna Cream on
super-fast and nutrient-packed
Whole-Grain Toast

Serves 2: 1 can water-packed tuna (6 oz) • Juice from 1/2 lemon • 2 tbs low-fat sour cream or yogurt • Salt to taste • Black pepper to taste • 4 slices whole-grain bread • 4 radishes • 2 tbs minced fresh chives

Thoroughly drain the tuna in a sieve, then use a hand blender or regular blender to finely puree the tuna with the lemon juice and sour cream. Season with salt and pepper. Toast the bread and spread with the tuna mixture. Wash and slice the radishes and arrange on top of the bread. Garnish with chives and serve.

Per Serving: 330 calories • 31 g protein • 5 g fat • 42 g carbohydrates

Fennel-Pineapple
with toasted pumpernickel bread
Salad

Mix the sour cream with the lime juice and milk and stir until smooth. Season with salt and pepper. Wash and trim the fennel bulb, then cut it into strips. Set aside some of the fennel leaves. Mix the fennel strips with the sour cream. Peel the pineapple, taking care to remove any remnants of the rind. Cut the pineapple in quarters lengthwise and remove the hard inner core. Dice the pineapple flesh, but do not add it to the sour cream/fennel mixture until shortly before serving. (Pineapple contains the enzyme bromelain, which can cause a bitter taste when mixed with dairy products.) Crumble the pumpernickel toast. Garnish the fennel/pineapple mixture with pumpernickel pieces and some of the fennel greens, and serve.

Serves 2:

2 tbs low-fat sour cream or plain yogurt

Juice from 1/2 lime

1–2 tbs milk

Salt to taste

Black pepper to taste

1 small bulb fennel

1/2 small pineapple (about 7 oz)

2 slices pumpernickel bread, toasted

Fennel

Aside from its fresh anise aroma, fennel offers active people a variety of highly valuable nutrients, such as vitamins A and E, calcium, and potassium. If you can, make sure to buy small bulbs, since the larger bulbs have tough outer leaves.

PER SERVING:

173 calories

6 g protein

3 g fat

34 g carbohydrates

Swordfish-Mango
an exotic source of energy
Ragout

Put the water in a saucepan, season lightly with salt, and bring it to a boil. Wash the rice, then add it to the boiling water, cover tightly, and simmer for 30–40 minutes. Peel and mince the onion. Cut the swordfish into 1/2-inch cubes. Peel the mango half, remove the pit if necessary, and dice. Briefly plunge the peach into boiling water and remove the skin with a sharp knife. Cut the peach in half, remove the pit, and cut the peach flesh into wedges.

Heat the peanut oil in a deep-sided nonstick skillet and sauté the onion over medium-low heat until golden brown. Add the diced fish and sauté, turning constantly. Add the stock, stir in the mustard, and simmer for 5 minutes over low heat. Season with salt and pepper. Add the fruit and heat for 2–3 minutes. Mix the cornstarch with the heavy cream, add to the ragout, and bring to a boil again briefly to thicken the sauce. Serve with the rice.

Serves 2:
1 1/4 cups water
Salt to taste
3/4 cup brown rice
1 small onion
10 oz swordfish (steaks or fillets)
1/2 fresh mango
1 fresh peach
2 tbs peanut oil
About 1 cup vegetable or fish stock
1 tbs hot mustard
Black pepper to taste
1 tsp cornstarch
2 tbs heavy cream

> **Nutritious fish**
> You can also use any other firm fish to prepare this dish—halibut, for instance. A crusty baguette or a serving of pasta make tasty alternatives to brown rice.

PER SERVING:
751 calories
38 g protein
29 g fat
83 g carbohydrates

Herb-Encrusted

with green beans and potatoes

Pike-Perch

Drizzle the lemon juice over the fish, cover, and let stand for 10 minutes. Preheat the oven to 400° F. Wash and peel the potatoes and cut into French-fry shapes. Wash and trim the beans, then simmer them in a generous amount of water with the potatoes until tender-crisp.

Peel and mince the garlic. Mix the garlic with 2 tbs of the butter, the parsley, bread crumbs, salt, and pepper. Brush the fish with the herb butter and bake in an ovenproof dish in the middle of the oven for 12–15 minutes, until the crust is crisp and the fish is cooked through.

Drain the beans and potatoes. Melt the remaining 2 tbs butter, add the savory, and toss with the beans and potatoes.

Arrange the fish on plates with a portion of the vegetables on the side, sprinkle with the Parmesan, and serve.

Serves 2:
Juice from 1/2 lemon
10 oz pike-perch fillets, or other mild white fish
10 oz potatoes
10 oz green beans
4 cloves garlic
1/3 cup butter (room temperature)
3 tbs minced fresh Italian parsley
About 2 tbs bread crumbs
Salt to taste
Black pepper to taste
2 tbs minced fresh savory
2 tbs freshly grated Parmesan cheese

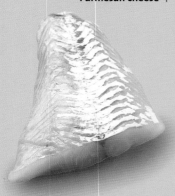

Pike-Perch

This tasty freshwater fish contains a generous amount of vitamin D, iodine, and selenium. With only 0.7 g of fat per 3 1/2 oz, it is practically fat free. Like vitamin E—a vitamin very important for athletes—selenium is an antioxidant. Selenium protects the cells from cancer-causing free radicals.

PER SERVING:

506 calories

41 g protein

21 g fat

38 g carbohydrates

Leek-Wrapped
rich in omega-3 fatty acids
Salmon Fillets

Trim the leek. Carefully remove 4 of the outer leaves, wash, and set aside. Cut the remaining leek in half lengthwise and wash it thoroughly. Slice the leek crosswise into half rings. Preheat the oven to 400° F. Bring a generous amount of salted water to a boil and boil the 4 set-aside leek leaves for 5 minutes. Use a slotted spoon to remove the leaves and let them drain. Add the fettuccine to the boiling leek water and cook according to the directions on the package.

Cut the bell pepper in half, remove the stem, seeds, and ribs, wash, and cut into strips. Heat the oil in a nonstick skillet. Briefly sauté the leek and the bell pepper strips over medium heat. Mix the sour cream and the crème fraîche, season with salt and pepper, and stir into the vegetables. Once the pasta is done, pour the pasta into a colander and let drain thoroughly. Mix the hot pasta with the vegetables, then pour the mixture into an oval casserole (about 11 inches long). Season the salmon fillets with salt and pepper, then wrap each piece with 2 of the blanched leek leaves (see cover photo). Place the packets seam-side down on top of the pasta. Distribute bits of the butter over the top of the casserole, cover, and bake in the middle of the oven for 20 minutes, until the salmon is cooked through.

Serves 2:
1 thick leek (about 9 oz)
Salt to taste
8 oz fettuccine
1 yellow bell pepper
1 tbs olive oil
1/4 cup sour cream
2 tbs crème fraîche
Black pepper to taste
2 salmon fillets (about 5 oz each)
1 tbs butter

PER SERVING: 886 calories • 47 g protein • 40 g fat • 83 g carbohydrates

Linguine with Smoked

sophisticated and nutritious fare

Trout and Basil

Serves 2:

Salt to taste

8 oz linguine

2 green onions

1 clove garlic

2 tsp capers (drained)

2 tsp butter

Scant 1/4 cup vegetable stock

1/2 cup crème fraîche

4 oz smoked trout

Fresh lemon juice to taste

Black pepper to taste

2 tbs minced fresh basil

Caper berries for garnish (optional)

Bring a generous amount of salted water to a boil and cook the linguine according to the directions on the package. Trim the green onions and peel the garlic. Cut the green onions into fine dice. Mince the capers.

For the sauce, heat the butter in a nonstick skillet and sauté the green onions over low heat until translucent. Mince the garlic and add it to the onions, then pour in the vegetable stock. Stir the capers and the crème fraîche into the skillet.

When the linguine is done, pour it into a colander and let drain. Pull the trout into pieces with your fingers, add it to the sauce, and heat over low heat. Season to taste with lemon juice, salt, and pepper, then stir in the linguine. Garnish with basil and caper berries, if using, and serve.

PER SERVING:

732 calories

29 g protein

27 g fat

92 g carbohydrates

Turkey Breast in
with mineral-rich wild rice and asparagus
Coconut Milk

Bring the water to a boil in a saucepan, seasoning it with salt. Wash the rice and add it to the boiling water. Cover and simmer over low heat for 35-40 minutes, until the liquid is absorbed.

Serves 2:

2 cups water

Salt to taste

3/4 cup wild rice

10 oz boneless turkey breast

White pepper to taste

8 oz asparagus

1/2 fresh pineapple (about 9 oz)

1/2 red chile

1 tbs vegetable oil

1 2/3 cups unsweetened coconut milk

1 tsp sambal oelek or other hot chile paste

3 tsp arrowroot

Season the turkey with salt and pepper, then cut it into thin strips. Peel the lower third of the asparagus stalks, then slice them diagonally into 1-inch pieces. Peel the pineapple, remove the hard core, and cut the flesh into cubes. Slit open the chile, remove the seeds, and cut the flesh into fine dice.

Heat the oil in a skillet. Brown the turkey strips in the oil over medium heat. Add the asparagus and cook for 3-5 minutes, stirring constantly. Stir in the coconut milk, sambal oelek, and chile and simmer over low heat for 6 more minutes. Dissolve the arrowroot in a little water and stir it into the contents of the skillet. Add the pineapple and cook until heated through. Serve with the wild rice.

Wild rice

Wild rice is actually the seed of American or Asian water grasses. It contains more protein, potassium, and magnesium than normal rice and should be a regular part of an athlete's diet. You can also find wild rice mixed with other types of rice.

PER SERVING:

897 calories

53 g protein

27 g fat

106 g carbohydrates

Apricot-Chicken

with bananas and basmati rice

Ragout

Put the water in a saucepan and season with salt. Add the rice and bring to a boil. Reduce the heat, cover the pan, and simmer for 12–15 minutes, until all of the water has been absorbed. Afterward, stir the rice and set aside the lid to let the steam escape. In the meantime, cut the chicken breasts into narrow strips, then season with salt, pepper, and curry powder. Peel and mince the ginger. Cut the chile in half lengthwise, remove the seeds, wash, and cut into fine dice.

Heat the oil in a deep-sided nonstick skillet. Brown the chicken strips, ginger, and chile in the oil over medium heat, stirring occasionally. Add the chicken stock and simmer over low heat for 3 minutes.

Peel the banana and cut it into thin slices. Wash the apricots, remove the pits, and cut the flesh into thin wedges. Add the banana, apricots, and raisins to the chicken mixture, stir, and heat through for 2-3 minutes. Arrange the rice on two plates, top with the ragout, and serve.

Serves 2:

1 1/4 cups water

Salt to taste

3/4 cup basmati rice

10 oz boneless, skinless chicken breasts

Black pepper to taste

1 tbs Madras curry powder

1 hazelnut-sized piece fresh ginger

1/2 red chile

2 tbs peanut oil

1 cup chicken stock

1 banana

5 fresh apricots

2 tbs raisins

Apricots—The beauty fruit

Apricots are rich in potassium, silicic acid, B-vitamins, and carotinoids, making them a powerhouse of nutrition. The same applies to dried apricots—a good reason to nibble on dried fruit instead of sweets when you feel like a snack.

PER SERVING:

780 calories

43 g protein

17 g fat

100 g carbohydrates

Pork Tenderloin in

an exotic dish with aromatic rice

Persimmon Sauce

Trim the sinews from the pork tenderloin, then season with salt and pepper. Heat the sesame oil in a nonstick skillet. Cook the pork in the oil over medium heat, turning to brown all sides, until almost cooked through, about 20 minutes. Put the water in a saucepan, season with salt, and bring to a boil. Wash the rice and add it to the boiling water with the raisins. Reduce the heat, cover the pan, and simmer for 12-15 minutes, until all of the water has been absorbed. Cut the chile in half lengthwise, remove the seeds, wash and cut into a fine dice. Peel the persimmon, cut in half, remove the seeds, and cut the flesh into fine dice. Dissolve the agar-agar in the vegetable stock.

Remove the pork from the skillet and wrap it in aluminum foil to keep it warm. Briefly sauté the chile and persimmon in the same pan as used for the pork, add the vegetable stock, and simmer over low heat until the broth is somewhat reduced. Divide the rice among 2 serving plates. Cut the meat in diagonal slices and arrange next to the rice. Pour the sauce over the meat and serve.

Serves 2:

1 small pork tenderloin (about 9 oz)

Salt to taste

Black pepper to taste

2 tbs sesame oil

1 1/2 cups water

3/4 cup jasmine rice

2 tbs raisins

1/2 red chile

1 ripe Hachiya persimmon

1 tsp agar-agar (health food store)

1 cup or more vegetable stock

Persimmons

Persimmons are an exotic, orange-colored fruit. They have a soft, jelly-like flesh and are easily digestible. They are rich in beta carotene and vitamin C. Be sure that the persimmon is very ripe or it will be far too astringent in the mouth. If desired, you can substitute half of a small, fresh pineapple (about 7 oz) for the persimmon in this recipe.

PER SERVING:

576 calories

33 g protein

12 g fat

80 g carbohydrates

Beef Fillets with

spicy, aromatic, and loaded with minerals

Green Beans

Peel the onion, garlic, and ginger and cut all into small dice. Remove the seeds from the chile, then wash and cut into a fine dice. Trim the leek, cut in half lengthwise, wash thoroughly, and then slice crosswise into half rings. Trim and wash the beans.

Serves 2:
1 small onion
3 cloves garlic
1 hazelnut-sized piece fresh ginger
1 green chile
1 leek
18 oz fresh green beans
2 tbs canola oil
1 tbs raw (turbinado) sugar
1 2/3 cups beef stock
2 small beef fillets (about 5 oz each)
Salt to taste
Black pepper to taste
1/4 cup sour cream
1 tbs cornstarch

Heat 1 tbs of the oil in a deep, nonstick skillet. Sauté the onion, garlic, ginger, and chile in the oil until the onion is translucent. Sprinkle the vegetables with the sugar and continue to stir until it is dissolved. Add the beef stock, leek, and green beans, cover, and simmer for about 10 minutes over low heat.

Using the flat side of a large chef's knife, firmly press the steaks and season with salt and pepper. Heat the remaining 1 tbs oil in a nonstick skillet over medium-high heat and brown the steaks for 4-8 minutes on each side, depending on desired doneness. Season the green beans with salt and pepper. Mix the sour cream and cornstarch together, stir into the vegetables, and let stand briefly. Arrange on a plate next to the steaks.

Green vegetables and meat

The combination of green vegetables and meat guarantees excellent iron absorption. In the human body, red blood cells are made up of up to 70 percent iron, and iron is responsible for the transportation of oxygen in the blood. This dish also contains 161 mg of magnesium and 1757 mg of potassium, which represent a large percentage of the recommended daily allowance of these minerals.

PER SERVING:
483 calories
41 g protein
23 g fat
28 g carbohydrates

Roast Beef on
rich in magnesium
Red Lentils

Peel and mince the green onions. Heat 1 tbs of the olive oil in a saucepan and sauté the onions over low heat until golden. Wash and sort the lentils, then add them to the onions. Add the beef stock. Cook the lentils over low heat for 8-10 minutes, until almost done.

In the meantime, cut the roast beef into strips. Heat the remaining 1 tbs oil in a nonstick skillet and brown the roast beef strips over medium heat until heated through.

Stir the minced chives into the yogurt, then season with salt and pepper. Season the lentils with the raspberry vinegar and add the roast beef. Arrange the mixture on 2 plates, garnishing with 1 tbs each of the chive yogurt. Pass the remaining yogurt in a separate dish.

Serves 2:

2 green onions

2 tbs olive oil

8 oz dried red lentils

1 2/3 cups beef stock

5 oz thinly sliced rare roast beef

1/4 cup minced fresh chives

6 oz low-fat plain yogurt

Salt to taste

Black pepper to taste

2 tbs raspberry vinegar

Lentils

Four ounces of lentils contains 129 mg of magnesium and 840 mg of potassium. In other words, when you eat a dish containing lentils, you have already met over one third of the recommended daily allowance of magnesium. Red lentils are particularly fast to prepare, taking only about 10 minutes to cook.

PER SERVING:

534 calories

45 g protein

14 g fat

58 g carbohydrates

Beef Fillets with
rich in iron and magnesium
Zucchini and Spaghetti

Bring a large pot of salted water to a boil. Add the spaghetti and cook according to the package directions. Peel the zucchini, then cut the zucchini diagonally into slices. Trim and cut the green onion into fine dice. Peel and mince the garlic.

Serves 2:
Salt to taste
4 oz spaghetti
1 zucchini
1 green onion
2-3 cloves garlic
2 beef steak fillets (about 5 oz each)
Black pepper to taste
2 tbs olive oil
2 tsp dried oregano
2 tbs sour cream

Using the flat side of a large chef's knife, firmly press the fillets and season with salt and pepper. Heat the oil in a nonstick skillet. Brown the steaks in the pan over medium heat for about 4-8 minutes per side, until cooked to desired doneness. Wrap the steaks in aluminum foil to keep warm. Drain the spaghetti thoroughly.

Using the same pan as for the meat, briefly sauté the green onion. Add the zucchini slices and sauté for a few minutes. Add the garlic and oregano and sauté until the garlic is transparent, stirring constantly. Stir in the sour cream and spaghetti and arrange with the steaks on plates.

Zucchini

Zucchini and other summer squash are high in vitamins A and C. They also boast a good amount of beta carotene, potassium, calcium, and niacin. Zucchini is a good vegetable choice for busy athletes because it cooks up quickly.

PER SERVING:

515 calories

41 g protein

19 g fat

45 g carbohydrates

Carrot-Spinach

a good source of potassium and vitamin E

Pancakes

Peel and wash the potatoes. Trim and peel the carrots. Using a large grater, grate the potatoes and carrots. Peel the onion and chop it finely. Sort through and wash the fresh spinach, remove any

Serves 2:

14 oz potatoes

4 oz carrots

1 small onion

8 oz fresh spinach (or 4 oz frozen spinach)

2 eggs

Black pepper to taste

2 tbs minced fresh marjoram

2 tbs canola oil

large stems, then cut the leaves into strips and steam them in a pot over medium heat until the spinach ceases to release water. If using frozen spinach, thaw it according to instructions and press out as much water as possible. In a large bowl, mix the potatoes, carrots, onions, and spinach with the eggs. Season with pepper and marjoram.

Heat the oil in a large, nonstick skillet (about 10 inches in diameter). Add the vegetable batter to the pan, smooth the top, and cook for 20 minutes over low heat. Carefully turn the pancake: gently slide the pancake onto a larger plate. Then, using a second plate, flip the pancake and carefully return it to the skillet. Cook the pancake for another 10-15 minutes. Cut the pancake into wedges and serve. These pancakes go well with a fresh salad.

Potatoes and eggs

The protein in potatoes is particularly well utilized by the body. When combined with eggs, the protein is even more valuable than protein derived from meat. Potatoes are rich in potassium. Use salt sparingly since salt contains sodium, which impairs the positive effects of potassium.

PER SERVING:

300 calories

13 g protein

15 g fat

27 g carbohydrates

Potato-Hamburger Casserole

easy to prepare

Preheat the oven to 400°F. Peel and wash the potatoes, then, using a mandoline or vegetable slicer, cut into very thin slices. Lightly cut a cross into the tops of the tomatoes and blanch for a few seconds in boiling water. After removing the tomatoes from the water, pull off the skins using a sharp knife and cut the flesh into slices. Wash the arugula, remove the stems, let drain well, then chop.

Heat the oil in a nonstick skillet. Brown the ground beef in the oil over high heat, stirring to break up large clumps, until no pink remains. Season with salt and pepper. Stir in the tomato paste, then set the pan aside. Drain the mozzarella and cut it into slices. Lightly oil an oval casserole pan (11 inches long) and layer in half of the potatoes. Add 1/2 of the ground beef mixture, then top with the arugula. Add the remaining potatoes, followed by the remaining ground beef. Top with the tomato slices and then with the mozzarella slices.

Mix the egg with the milk and the cinnamon. Pour the milk mixture over the contents of the casserole. Bake in the middle of the oven for about 55 minutes until the potatoes are tender. If necessary, cover the pan with aluminum foil to prevent the mozzarella from becoming overly browned. Let stand for 5 minutes before serving.

Serves 2:
1 lb potatoes
4 vine-ripened tomatoes (about 14 oz)
1 bunch arugula (about 2 oz)
1 tbs canola oil
10 oz ground beef
Salt to taste
Black pepper to taste
2 tbs tomato paste
4 oz fresh mozzarella cheese
Oil for the casserole pan
1 egg
6 tbs low-fat milk
1 tsp ground cinnamon

PER SERVING: 565 calories • 50 g protein • 22 g fat • 40 g carbohydrates

Gnocchi with Oyster Mushrooms

a fast, easy source of minerals

Cook the gnocchi according to package directions in a generous amount of salted water. Trim the green onion and chop finely. Cut the ham into thin strips. Trim and wash the oyster mushrooms, then cut into strips.

Heat the butter in a deep nonstick skillet. Add the green onion and ham and sauté over medium heat until the onions are golden. Add the oyster mushrooms and sauté for 3–4 minutes over low heat, stirring constantly.

Using a slotted spoon, remove the gnocchi when done and let drain in a colander. Add the heavy cream and milk to the mushrooms, then season to taste with salt and pepper. Reduce the cream mixture over low heat for 1-2 minutes. Stir the Parmesan and gnocchi into the mushroom mixture. Arrange the gnocchi on plates, garnish with the chives, and serve immediately.

Serves 2:

1 lb prepared potato gnocchi (fresh, from the refrigerated section)
Salt to taste
1 green onion
4 oz lean cooked ham
8 oz oyster mushrooms
1 tbs butter
3 tbs heavy cream
6 tbs low-fat milk
Black pepper to taste
2 tbs freshly grated Parmesan cheese
2 tbs minced fresh chives

Mushrooms

Mushrooms are rich in potassium, contain some magnesium and iron. Some are rich in niacin, a nutrient that plays an important role when it comes to energy conversion. You should only buy mushrooms that are firm and do not have any moist areas. Prepare mushrooms on the same day you buy them, since they lose much of their nutrients when they are stored.

PER SERVING:

390 calories

20 g protein

20 g fat

31 g carbohydrates

Vitamin Diet

Get Slim
healthy and beautiful
and Fit

How to Achieve your Goal

We all want to be slim and healthy. And we all know that traditional diets are no help. Actually, all you need to reach this goal is a carefully chosen eating plan. Also, make sure you get enough exercise and don't overtax your body with too much alcohol, tobacco, or other toxins. On the following pages you'll find the eating plan you're looking for, featuring simple, flavorful recipes that are packed full of vitamins. Now that you're getting your daily supply of vitamins from your food, you can say goodbye to supplements.

Nature's Miracles

We cannot see vitamins, and yet we cannot survive without them. To thrive, our bodies need a certain amount of vitamins every day. These tiny little miracles provide no calories, but they function as our body's "laborers." Vitamins are involved in every metabolic process, are essential for the reproduction of cells, and strengthen our immune systems. In short: vitamins keep us healthy and happy. If we don't get enough of them, we soon start to feel weak and fall ill.

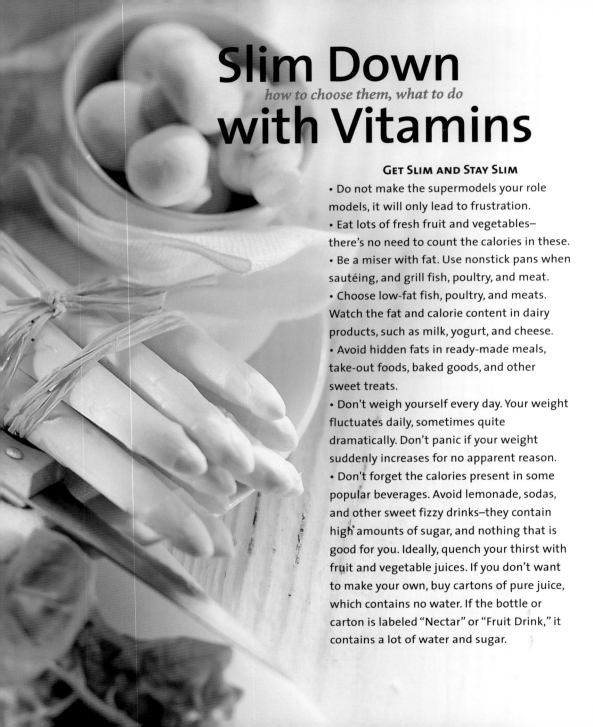

Slim Down
how to choose them, what to do
with Vitamins

GET SLIM AND STAY SLIM

• Do not make the supermodels your role models, it will only lead to frustration.

• Eat lots of fresh fruit and vegetables– there's no need to count the calories in these.

• Be a miser with fat. Use nonstick pans when sautéing, and grill fish, poultry, and meat.

• Choose low-fat fish, poultry, and meats. Watch the fat and calorie content in dairy products, such as milk, yogurt, and cheese.

• Avoid hidden fats in ready-made meals, take-out foods, baked goods, and other sweet treats.

• Don't weigh yourself every day. Your weight fluctuates daily, sometimes quite dramatically. Don't panic if your weight suddenly increases for no apparent reason.

• Don't forget the calories present in some popular beverages. Avoid lemonade, sodas, and other sweet fizzy drinks–they contain high amounts of sugar, and nothing that is good for you. Ideally, quench your thirst with fruit and vegetable juices. If you don't want to make your own, buy cartons of pure juice, which contains no water. If the bottle or carton is labeled "Nectar" or "Fruit Drink," it contains a lot of water and sugar.

Treat Vitamins with Care

Vitamins need to be treated with a little TLC. Light, air, and heat will destroy them, so the following rules should be observed– especially in the case of fruit and vegetables:

* use as soon as possible
* if you need to store them, keep them in a cool and dark place
* do not peel or chop fruits or vegetables until just before cooking and/or eating
* wash as quickly as possible
* wash first, then chop or slice so that water-soluble vitamins do not leach out
* cook fruit and vegetables as little as possible; in order to retain the most vitamins, eat fruit and vegetables raw
* steam fruit and vegetables under a tightly fitting lid, in their own juices, or in just a tiny amount of liquid
* serve as soon as possible

Even just for preserving vitamins, it is worth investing in a steamer, or a steamer insert for a saucepan. Use only a small amount of water. Place the vegetables in the steamer insert, place the insert in the saucepan, cover with a lid, and steam over medium heat until just tender-crisp.

What Destroys Vitamins?

Vitamin	Main Enemies
A	light, air
D	reasonably resilient vitamin
E	light, air, heat
K	reasonably resilient vitamin
B_1	heat, water
B_2	light, water
B_6	heat, water, cold
B_{12}	light, air, water
Niacin	water
Folic acid	light, heat, water (very sensitive)
Pantothenic acid	heat, water, acid,
Biotin	water
C	light, air, heat water

Important: Do not leave newly bought fruit and vegetables unwrapped or at room temperature for longer than absolutely necessary. Use organic produce whenever possible.

Vitamins for Better Health

Vitamin	Good Sources
A	Green-leafed vegetables, yellow and red fruits and vegetables, eggs, butter, liver
D	Liver, meat, milk, fish, eggs, mushrooms
E	Vegetable fats (especially wheat germ and sunflower oils), cabbage, bell peppers, spinach, salsify, avocados, cereals/grains, nuts
K	Green vegetables, whole-grain breads and cereals, milk, meat
B_1	Sprouts, whole-grain breads and cereals, potatoes, sunflower seeds, egg yolks, pork, yeast
B_2	Sprouts, milk, whole-grain breads and cereals, meat, fish
B_6	Cabbage, leeks, bell peppers, soybeans, bananas, whole-grain breads and cereals, potatoes, nuts, meat, fish
B_{12}	Meat, vegetables containing lactic acid, milk, sour milk products, eggs, fish
Niacin	Potatoes, mushrooms, peas, whole-grain breads and cereals, meats, fish
Folic acid	Spinach, asparagus, fennel, beets, potatoes, orange juice, whole-grain breads and cereals, milk
Pantothenic acid	Broccoli, mushrooms, melons, egg yolks, whole-grain breads and cereals, yeast, liver, meat, milk, mushrooms
Biotin	Carrots, peas, sprouts, spinach, tofu, eggs, yeast, nuts, oats, milk, whole-grain breads and cereals, mushrooms
C	Citrus fruits, berries, kiwi, bell peppers, cabbage, spinach, potatoes

NEEDED FOR	SIGNS OF A DEFICIENCY	VITAMIN
Eye, skin, and hair health; cell protection; disease resistance; protection against cancer	Poor night vision; flaky skin; poor resistance to infection	A
Bone and skin health	Growth problems; decalcification of bones	D
Cell protection; liver detoxification; protection against cancer and heart disease (antioxidant)	Anemia; paleness; muscular weakness	E
Blood coagulation	Slow coagulation of blood	K
Release of energy from carbohydrates; combating stress; heart and muscle health; memory	Tiredness; loss of appetite; muscular, circulatory, and coronary weakness; cramps; poor performance	B_1
Converting proteins, fats and carbohydrates into energy; growth; disease resistance	Cracks on lips and at corners of mouth; dry skin; poor vitality	B_2
Protein metabolism; growth; skin, hair and nerve health; reproduction of blood cells	Tiredness; anemia; skin changes; loss of appetite	B_6
Cell construction and protection; disease resistance; reproduction of blood cells and tissues; growth	Anemia; tiredness; poor resistance to infections	B_{12}
Energy release in tissues and cells; skin, heart, and nerve health; growth	Nausea; diarrhea; depression	Niacin
Growth and reproduction of cells, particularly red blood cells; protection against heart attacks	Anemia; tiredness; poor resistance to infections	Folic acid
Releasing energy from foods; bones, skin, and hair health; hormone creation	Skin damage; dull hair; nervousness; poor resistance to infections	Pantothenic acid
Metabolism of carbohydrates, proteins, and fats; blood, nerve, skin, and hair health	Lethargy; loss of appetite; loss of hair; skin changes	Biotin
Immune system health; iron absorption; reproduction of blood cells; cell construction	Poor resistance to infection; lethargy; slow-healing wounds; growth problems; poor performance	C

Power

highly nutritious low-calorie meals

Week

GET SLIM & BE FIT

Are you feeling listless, weak, and tired? Would you like to lose a few pounds? Follow the menu suggestions given in our "Power Week" for just seven days, and you won't have to wait long to see the results!

THE PLAN

Following are meal suggestions for each day of the week, which you can follow as given or switch around to suit your whim. For the best start to your day, make a delicious breakfast of whole-grain flakes or coarsely ground cereal, fresh fruit, and low-fat yogurt after your shower. Those of us with a sweet tooth can add a tiny bit of honey or maple syrup. Or, spread some low-fat cottage cheese on a slice of whole-grain bread. Eat as much fresh fruit and vegetables as you like between meals. Quench your thirst with fruit and herbal teas, and mineral water with fruit juice for extra flavor and vitamins.

FOR BUSY PEOPLE

If you are unable to prepare two meals a day, choose a recipe and prepare it in the evening to eat the next day. Bring fresh fruit and low-fat, low-sugar yogurt for your lunch break. You can also take instant broth granules and add boiling water for a warming soup. Soothe any between-meal hunger pangs with an apple, some raw vegetables, or an occasional whole-grain roll.

The Week's Meals

Monday

* Muesli with fresh fruit, or whole-grain bread
* Vegetable and Herb Salad, whole-grain roll
* Spanish Potato Tortilla * Date and Pineapple Salad

Tuesday

* Blueberry and Banana Milk, whole-grain bread
* Curried Ginger Vegetables, brown rice
* Cauliflower and Broccoli Salad

Wednesday

* Muesli with fresh fruit, or whole-grain bread
* Indonesian Vegetable Soup * Iced Pineapple and Almond Shake
* Fruited Raw Carrots * Stovetop Spelt Cakes with Radishes

Thursday

* Raspberry and Strawberry Shake, whole-grain bread
* Spinach Salad with Oranges, whole-grain baguette
* Turnip and Turkey Fricassee, brown rice

Friday

* Muesli with fresh fruit, or whole-grain bread
* Stir-Fried Thai Vegetables, rice noodles
* Zucchini and Tomato Salad, rye baguette * Jellied Fruit Tea with Grapes

Saturday

* Carrot and Tomato Yogurt, whole-grain bread
* Vegetable and Sprout Salad, whole-grain bread or roll
* Linguine with Raw Tomato Sauce * Citrus Fruit Platter

Sunday

* fruit salad, whole-grain roll, low-fat cheese, and an egg
* Asparagus Salad * Strawberry and Kiwi Salad
* Light Minestrone, whole-grain bread or roll

Spinach

and toasted

Salad with

pine nuts

Oranges

Serves 2: 2 oranges • 4 oz fresh spinach • 1 small red onion • 1-2 tbs red wine vinegar • Salt to taste • Black pepper to taste • 3 tbs olive oil • 1 tbs pine nuts (toasted)

Peel the oranges and cut into segments. Wash and pick over the spinach, discarding any coarse stalks. Peel and halve the onion and slice thinly.

In a salad bowl, combine the vinegar, salt, pepper, and oil. Stir the oranges, spinach, and onion into the dressing. Sprinkle with the toasted pine nuts.

power

PER PORTION: 195 calories • 3 g protein • 14 g fat • 16 g carbohydrates

Vegetable and
with cashew nuts and fresh ginger
Sprout Salad

Roughly chop the cashew nuts and toast them in a dry nonstick pan until golden. Remove from the pan and set aside.

Serves 2:
2 tbs cashew nuts
Thumb-sized piece fresh ginger
1 small shallot
2 tbs sherry vinegar
Salt to taste
White pepper to taste
3 tbs sunflower oil
1 tbs sesame oil
1 small carrot
1 radish
2 oz cucumber
4 oz mixed sprouts

Peel and finely chop the ginger and shallots. Combine both with the vinegar, salt, and pepper, then add the two oils, and beat well.

Trim and peel the carrot, radish, and cucumber and grate coarsely. Rinse the sprouts in a sieve, drain well, and tear into bite-sized pieces. Combine with the grated vegetables, mix with the dressing, and arrange on two plates. Sprinkle with the toasted cashew nuts and serve immediately.

Sprouts

Set up your own little sprout farm on the windowsill so you have a constant supply of fresh vitamins. Fresh sprouts are full of beta carotene, vitamins E and K, and various B complex vitamins–including the rare B_{12}.

PER PORTION:

244 calories

4 g protein

22 g fat

9 g carbohydrates

power

Cauliflower and Broccoli Salad

with creamy nutmeg sauce

Toast the almonds in a dry skillet until brown, then remove. Trim and wash the cauliflower and broccoli and cut into bite-sized florets. Peel and chop the broccoli stalks. Place the vegetables in a steamer insert.

Bring the stock to a boil in a saucepan. Place the steamer insert inside, cover tightly, and steam the vegetables over low heat for 5 minutes.

In a bowl, beat together the egg yolk, lemon juice, nutmeg, salt, and pepper. Place the bowl over a pot of lightly boiling water and stir the ingredients. Gradually add the hot stock, stirring constantly, until you have a fairly thick sauce. Set the bowl aside.

Wash, dry, and chop the parsley and add to the sauce. Season the sauce and pour over the cauliflower and broccoli. Sprinkle with the sliced almonds and serve immediately.

Serves 2:
1 tbs sliced almonds
9 oz cauliflower
7 oz broccoli
1/2 cup vegetable stock
1 egg yolk
1-2 tsp fresh lemon juice
Freshly ground nutmeg
Salt to taste
Black pepper to taste
1 sprig fresh Italian parsley

Vegetable stock

You can easily make your own fresh stock using onions, mushrooms, carrots, celery, tomatoes, seasonings and herbs.

Sauté chopped onions and mushrooms until they turn dark. Chop the other vegetables and bring to a boil in about 1 quart of water with the seasonings of your choice. Simmer for one hour and let cool. Strain.

PER PORTION: 189 calories • 11 g protein • 10 g fat • 17 g carbohydrates

Zucchini and

with stuffed zucchini blossoms

Tomato Salad

2 zucchini blossoms (with
baby zucchini attached)
3 small shallots
1 small carrot
1 tsp olive oil
3 oz ricotta cheese
Salt to taste
Black pepper to taste
1/2 tsp mustard
1 tbs white wine vinegar
2-3 tbs extra virgin olive oil
5 oz baby zucchini
3 small, firm tomatoes

Preheat the oven to 350°F. Shake the zucchini blossoms, then gently pull out the pistils from the centers. Peel and finely chop 1 shallot. Peel and grate the carrot. Heat the oil in a small nonstick skillet and gently sauté the chopped shallot and grated carrot over low heat for a few minutes. In a bowl, mix together the ricotta, sautéed carrot, and shallot, salt, and pepper. Using a teaspoon, carefully fill the zucchini blossoms with the ricotta mixture and fold the petals over the filling. Place the stuffed blossoms in a baking dish and bake in the center of the oven for about 10 minutes, turning once halfway through.

Meanwhile, to make the dressing, peel and chop the remaining 2 shallots and mix with some salt and pepper, the mustard, and vinegar; then beat in the oil.

Wash and trim the zucchini. Wash the tomatoes and remove the stalks. Cut the tomatoes and zucchini into thin slices and arrange on two plates. Pour over the dressing, place the stuffed zucchini blossoms on top, and serve.

PER PORTION: 225 calories • 7 g protein • 18 g fat • 9 g carbohydrates

Vegetable and

with cider vinegar dressing

Herb Salad

In a salad bowl, combine the cider vinegar, salt, and pepper; then, add both oils and beat thoroughly. Season well.

Serves 2:
2 tbs cider vinegar
Salt to taste
White pepper to taste
2 tbs canola oil
1 tbs walnut oil
1 small kohlrabi
10 radishes
3 oz baby carrots
3 oz cucumber
2 green onions
1 tbs walnut halves
1/2 bunch fresh Italian parsley
1/2 bunch fresh basil

Peel the kohlrabi and trim and wash the radishes. Set aside some of the tender kohlrabi and radish leaves.

Trim, wash, and peel the carrots. Wash or peel the cucumber. Cut the vegetables into very small dice, or slice thinly.

Trim, wash, and finely slice the green onions. Chop the walnut halves. Wash, shake dry, and chop the reserved vegetable leaves, parsley, and basil.

Carefully stir the vegetables, walnuts, and herbs into the dressing and season the salad again with salt and pepper.

Getting ahead of yourself

You can prepare this salad 1 or 2 hours ahead of time and let it stand. Cover the bowl well with plastic wrap and refrigerate until serving time to avoid vitamin loss.

PER PORTION:

271 calories

11 g protein

14 g fat

26 g carbohydrates

power

Coleslaw with
high in folic acid
Red Onions

Peel and finely chop the onion and combine in a bowl with the vinegars, salt, and pepper. Wash the cress, thyme, and marjoram. Chop the cress and strip the stalks of the thyme and the marjoram. Add the herb leaves to the vinegar mixture, then add the two oils, and beat well.

Trim, wash, and coarsely grate the cabbage. Either use it raw, or blanch in a little salted boiling water for 3-4 minutes. Drain well, then add it to the bowl. Toss well and let stand for about 30 minutes.

Wash and dry the pear. Cut it into quarters and remove the core. Slice the quarters widthwise and toss it in the lemon juice. Arrange on the coleslaw and serve.

Serves 2:
1 red onion
1 tbs cider vinegar
1 tbs white wine vinegar
Salt to taste
Black pepper to taste
1/2 bunch peppercress
1-2 sprigs fresh thyme
1-2 sprigs fresh marjoram
2 tbs sunflower oil
1 tbs pumpkin seed oil
10 oz green cabbage
1 pear
1 tbs fresh lemon juice

Green cabbage

Green cabbage is a good source of folic acid, which is beneficial just before and during the early stages of pregnancy. Cabbage also contains other B vitamins and carotene. Eat it raw for maximum nutritional benefit.

PER PORTION:
246 calories
4 g protein
13 g fat
30 g carbohydrates

power

Asparagus Salad

with piquant tomato vinaigrette

Wash the tomato and remove the stalk. Cut it into eighths, remove the seeds, and finely dice. Wash the chives briefly, dry thoroughly, and chop thinly.

In a bowl, mix the apple syrup or honey with the cider vinegar, salt, and pepper. Add the two oils and beat thoroughly. Add the tomato and chives and stir carefully.

Wash and trim the asparagus and peel the lower third. Cut it diagonally into very thin slices and immediately toss it in the dressing. Arrange on plates.

Wash and shake dry the basil. Roughly chop the pistachio nuts. Sprinkle the basil leaves and the pistachio nuts over the salad and serve immediately.

Serves 2:
1 firm tomato
1/2 bunch fresh chives
2 tbs apple syrup, or
1 tbs honey
1 tbs cider vinegar
Salt to taste
White pepper to taste
1 1/2 tbs vegetable oil
2 tbs pistachio oil
10 oz green asparagus
Small fresh basil leaves
2 tbs pistachio nuts

Asparagus

This elegant vegetable is very low in calories–only about 54 calories per 10 oz–and very is high in vitamins A, C, B$_1$, and B$_2$. The presence of calcium, phosphorous, potassium, and iodine add to the value of this healthy food. Aspartic acid stimulates kidney activity, making asparagus a good diuretic.

PER PORTION:

248 calories

4 g protein

23 g fat

6 g carbohydrates

Fruited

with grapefruit and apple syrup

Raw Carrots

Serves 2: 1 grapefruit • 2 tbs pumpkin seed oil • 1 tbs cider vinegar • 2 tbs apple syrup or 1 tbs honey • Salt to taste • Black pepper to taste • 7 oz carrots • 2 tbs pumpkin seeds

Carefully peel the grapefruit and cut it into segments, collecting the juice in a bowl. Combine the juice with the oil, vinegar, and apple syrup or honey, and stir until smooth. Season with salt and pepper. Peel, trim, and coarsely grate the carrots. Mix with the dressing and arrange on plates with the grapefruit segments. Sprinkle with the pumpkin seeds.

PER PORTION: 196 calories • 6 g protein • 14 g fat • 13 g carbohydrates

Beet

winter power source

Salad

Serves 2: 4 small fresh beets • 1/2 bunch fresh Italian parsley • 1 tsp mustard • 2 tbs white wine vinegar • Salt to taste • Black pepper to taste • 3 tbs olive oil • 2 tbs sliced almonds (toasted)

Wash and scrub the beets thoroughly. Place the unpeeled beets in boiling water and cook for about 30 minutes, until tender. Wash, shake dry, and chop the parsley. Mix with the mustard, vinegar, salt, and pepper; then, beat in the oil. Peel the beets, cut into slices, and then into thick strips. Stir them into the dressing and sprinkle with almonds before serving.

PER PORTION: 190 calories • 3 g protein • 16 g fat • 9 g carbohydrates

Brussels Sprout Salad
and spicy horseradish
with Fresh Pears

Wash and trim the Brussels sprouts and cut an X into the base of the stalks with a paring knife.

Bring the stock to a boil in a saucepan. Place the Brussels sprouts in a steamer insert and place in the saucepan. Cover with a tightly fitting lid and steam over low heat for about 5 minutes.

Peel and core the pear and coarsely grate the flesh. Place in a dish, and immediately add the lemon juice, crème fraîche, and a small amount of the vegetable stock. Whip the cream until stiff and gently fold into the dressing. Stir in the horseradish, and season with salt and pepper.

Cut the roast beef into thick strips, arrange on plates with the Brussels sprouts, and pour the dressing over the top.

Serves 2:
8 oz baby Brussels sprouts
1/2 cup vegetable stock
1 small pear
1 tbs fresh lemon juice
2 tbs crème fraîche
3 tbs heavy cream
2 tsp grated fresh horseradish
Salt to taste
Black pepper to taste
2 oz roast beef, thinly sliced

PER PORTION: 252 calories • 11 g protein • 14 g fat • 24 g carbohydrates

Vegetable
with radish vinaigrette
Vitamins

Wash and peel the carrots and horseradish. Wash the zucchini. Grate the carrots, horseradish, and zucchini coarsely, or cut into thin slices. Wash the tomato, remove the stalk, and cut into slices. Wash, trim, and thinly slice the green onion.

Serves 2:
4 oz carrots
1 small piece fresh
horseradish root
1 small zucchini
1 tomato
1 green onion
6 radishes
1 tbs lemon juice
2 tsp apple syrup, or
1 tsp honey
2 tbs cider vinegar
2 tbs sunflower oil
2 tbs olive oil
Salt to taste
Black pepper to taste
1 tbs sunflower kernels

Wash and trim the radishes and leaves. Chop a small amount of the tender radish leaves and set aside. Slice half of the radishes, and coarsely grate the rest.

Combine the chopped radish leaves with the lemon juice, apple syrup or honey, and cider vinegar in a bowl. Beat in the two oils. Stir in the grated radishes, then season the dressing with salt and pepper.

Arrange the remaining ingredients on a serving dish or two individual plates. Pour the radish vinaigrette over the salad and sprinkle with the sunflower kernels.

Radishes and horseradish

These "cousins" contain a generous amount of vitamin C, as well as several other essential vitamins and minerals. Because they are usually eaten raw, you get the maximum benefit from the nutrients.

PER PORTION:

300 calories

9 g protein

19 g fat

23 g carbohydrates

power

Light
the classic Italian soup
Minestrone

Wash, peel, and dice the potatoes. Wash, trim, and chop the leek, zucchini, carrots, and fennel.

Wash the tomato and carefully cut an X into the round end. Place in boiling water for a few moments, then peel and chop roughly, discarding the core. Peel and finely chop the onion.

In a saucepan, heat the oil over medium-low heat and sauté the chopped onion until translucent. Add the fennel, carrots, leek, and zucchini, and sauté gently. Add the stock. Add the tomato and the potatoes. Cover the pan tightly and cook over medium heat for about 20 minutes.

Wash and shake dry the herbs. Remove the leaves from the coarse stalks and chop. Add the herbs to the soup and season with salt and pepper.

Sprinkle with the grated cheese before serving.

Serves 2:
6 oz boiling potatoes
1 baby leek
4 oz zucchini
4 oz carrots
1/2 bulb fennel
1 large tomato
1 small onion
1 tbs olive oil
2 cups hot stock
1/2 bunch fresh Italian parsley
1/2 bunch fresh basil
Salt to taste
Black pepper to taste
1 oz Romano cheese, freshly grated

power

PER PORTION: 394 calories • 17 g protein • 13 g fat • 54 g carbohydrates

Chilled Spanish

refreshing and full of vitamins

Vegetable Soup

Carefully cut an X into the round ends of the tomatoes. Place in boiling water for a few moments, then peel and chop, discarding the core. Peel the onion and the cucumber. Halve, trim, and wash the pepper. Finely

Serves 2:

10 oz ripe tomatoes

1 small Spanish onion

1/2 cucumber

1 small green bell pepper

2 cloves garlic

1/2-1 tbs red wine vinegar

1 slice white bread

2 tbs extra virgin olive oil

Salt to taste

Black pepper to taste

dice the vegetables. Peel the garlic and place in a blender with the tomatoes and a generous half of the other vegetables. Puree until smooth.

Sprinkle the vinegar and about 1/2 cup water over the bread and let stand for a few minutes. Add to the pureed vegetables with the oil, and puree until smooth. Season with salt and pepper and cover with plastic wrap. Place in the refrigerator to chill for about 30 minutes. Cover the remaining vegetables and place in the refrigerator to chill.

Stir the soup and season. Stir in the remaining vegetables and serve immediately.

Refreshing sources of vitamins

Cold soups are invigorating on hot summer days, and provide generous amounts of vitamins. The vegetables are processed raw, so that most of the vitamins are retained. It is important to cover and chill the soup to let the flavors develop fully.

PER PORTION:

187 calories

5 g protein

9 g fat

23 g carbohydrates

power

Indonesian
with celery and bean sprouts
Vegetable Soup

Pour a generous amount of hot water over the noodles in a bowl and let stand until softened.

Bring 2 cups water to a boil. Wash the chicken and place in the water. Wash the lemon under hot water and remove the zest. Peel and finely chop the ginger. Place both in the water with the chicken, bay leaf, and peanuts. Cover and simmer over low heat for about 30 minutes.

Rinse the bean sprouts under cold water and shake dry. Wash and trim the celery and the green onions. Wash and peel the carrot. Cut the vegetables into thin slices.

Remove the chicken from the stock. Discard the skin and bones and cut the meat into thin slices. Strain the stock and heat through again. Season to taste with soy sauce, pepper, and the juice from the zested lemon. Place the chicken, drained noodles, and sliced vegetables in the stock and cook for 3-4 minutes. Sprinkle with the cilantro leaves and serve.

Serves 2:
3/4 oz cellophane noodles
4-5 chicken legs
1 small lemon
1/2 oz fresh ginger
1 bay leaf
1 tbs roasted peanuts
3 oz bean sprouts
2 stalks celery
2 green onions
1 carrot
2-3 tbs light soy sauce
White pepper to taste
Handful of fresh cilantro leaves

PER PORTION: 567 calories • 53 g protein • 30 g fat • 23 g carbohydrates

Cream of
full of vitamin C and fiber
Radish Soup

Thoroughly wash the radishes and leaves. Set some of the tender leaves and 2-3 radishes aside. Roughly chop the remaining radish leaves and the remaining radishes.

Peel and finely dice the shallot. Wash, peel, and roughly chop the potatoes.

Heat the oil in a saucepan over medium heat, add the shallot, and sauté until translucent. Add the chopped radishes, chopped radish leaves, and potatoes and sauté briefly. Pour in the stock. Cover the pan tightly and simmer gently over medium heat for about 20 minutes.

Puree the soup in a blender until smooth. Return the soup to the saucepan and heat through. Stir in 1 tbs of the crème fraîche and season with salt and pepper.

Thinly slice the reserved radishes and radish leaves.

Pour the soup into two bowls and spoon the remaining crème fraîche into the centers. Sprinkle with the radish slices and leaves.

Serves 2:
1 large bunch radishes
1 shallot
4 oz potatoes
2 tbs sunflower oil
1 1/4 cups vegetable stock
2 tbs crème fraîche
Salt to taste
White pepper to taste

power

PER PORTION: 153 calories• 2 g protein• 9 g fat • 14 g carbohydrates

Rutabaga Stew
with Meatballs
with lots of carotene and vitamin C

In a bowl, mix together the ground beef, egg, bread crumbs, salt, pepper, and cayenne pepper. Shape into small meatballs.

Serves 2:
6 oz lean ground beef
1 egg
2-3 tbs bread crumbs
Salt to taste
Black pepper to taste
Cayenne pepper to taste
14 oz rutabaga
1 leek
2 cups vegetable stock
1-2 tsp vegetable oil
1/2 bunch fresh basil
1/2-1 tsp curry powder
1/2 tsp ground cumin

Trim and peel the rutabaga. Cut into thin slices, then into thin strips. Trim the leek, slice lengthwise, and wash thoroughly. Shake dry and cut into thin slices. In a saucepan, bring the stock to a boil. Place the rutabaga and leek in the stock, cover tightly, and simmer gently over low heat for about 10 minutes. Meanwhile, heat the oil over medium heat in a small nonstick skillet. Brown the meatballs on all sides in the oil, about 10 minutes.

Wash and shake dry the basil, setting aside some of the leaves for garnish. Finely chop the remaining leaves and add to the pan with the vegetables.

Season with the curry, cumin, salt, and pepper. Add the meatballs and garnish with the reserved basil.

Rutabagas
Rutabagas, a cross between turnips and cabbage, contain generous amounts of vitamins and minerals, and are especially high in carotene, niacin, vitamin B$_6$, and vitamin C.

PER PORTION:
464 calories
35 g protein
17 g fat
44 g carbohydrates

power

Sauerkraut Soup
high in vitamin C
with Chive Cream

Serves 2: 1 small onion • 1 small potato • 1 tbs butter • 5 oz sauerkraut (drained) • 2 cups vegetable stock • Salt to taste • Black pepper to taste • 1 bunch fresh chives • 3 tbs sour cream

Peel and finely dice the onion and potato, and sauté both in the butter in a saucepan until the onion is translucent. Add the sauerkraut and the stock, cover, and simmer gently for about 10 minutes. Puree the mixture and season well. Pour back into the saucepan and heat through. Wash and chop the chives and combine with the sour cream, salt, and pepper. Pour over the soup before serving.

PER PORTION: 253 calories • 7 g protein • 11 g fat • 33 g carbohydrates

Creamy
with toasted almonds
Leek Soup

Serves 2: 1 leek • 4 oz potatoes • 1 cup vegetable stock • Salt to taste • White pepper to taste • 1 tsp fresh thyme leaves • 3 tbs plain yogurt • 2 tbs sliced almonds (toasted)

Cut the leek in half lengthwise, wash, trim, and cut into slices. Peel, wash, and finely chop the potatoes. Place both in a saucepan with the stock, cover tightly, and simmer gently for 15 minutes. Puree the soup and season with salt, pepper, and the thyme. Pour back into the saucepan and heat through. Stir in the yogurt and garnish with the almonds.

PER PORTION: 187 calories • 8 g protein • 7 g fat • 24 g carbohydrates

Curried Ginger
with chile and coconut milk
Vegetables

Slit open the chile, trim, wash, and cut into thin rings. Peel and finely chop the garlic and ginger. Wash, trim, and slice the green onions. Wash and trim the snow peas and cut into thirds diagonally. Wash and peel the carrots. Cut into thin strips lengthwise, then slice as thinly as possible. Rinse the bean sprouts in a sieve and drain well.

Heat the oil in a wok over medium-high heat. Add the garlic, ginger, and chile rings and stir-fry lightly. Add the snow peas and carrots and stir-fry for 2-3 minutes. Then, add the green onions and stir-fry for a minute or two. Add the coconut milk, curry paste, and soy sauce and heat through. Add the bean sprouts and heat for another 1-2 minutes. Wash and roughly chop a few cilantro leaves. Sprinkle over the vegetables and serve immediately.

Serves 2:
1 red chile
1 clove garlic
Thumb-sized piece fresh ginger
1/2 bunch green onions
4 oz snow peas
5 oz carrots
3 oz fresh bean sprouts
1 tbs vegetable oil
1 cup unsweetened coconut milk
1-2 tsp hot curry paste
3 tbs light soy sauce
Fresh cilantro leaves

PER PORTION: 234 calories • 6 g protein • 16 g fat • 19 g carbohydrates

Stir-Fried Squash
with curry, chiles, and grapes
with Brown Rice

In a saucepan, gently heat 1/2 tbs of the olive oil over medium heat. Stir in the rice, then pour in the stock and cover tightly. Cook over low heat until just firm to the bite (20-40 minutes, depending on the type of rice; refer to the instructions on the package).

Serves 2:
2 tbs extra virgin olive oil
1/2 cup brown rice
1 cup vegetable stock
About 1 lb butternut squash
Salt to taste
1/2 bunch green onions
1-2 small red chiles
1 small clove garlic
2 oz seedless green grapes
1/4-1/2 tbs curry powder
Black pepper to taste
2-3 tbs pumpkin seeds

Peel the squash and remove the seeds and tough fibers. Cut the squash flesh into 1/2-3/4-inch pieces. Bring 1/2 cup of lightly salted water to a boil in a saucepan. Place the squash in the boiling water, cover tightly and cook for about 5 minutes. Drain, reserving the cooking liquid.

Wash and trim the green onions and cut them diagonally into thin rings. Trim the chiles, remove the seeds, rinse, and finely chop. Peel and finely chop the garlic. Rinse the grapes under hot water.

Heat the remaining 1 tbs oil in a wok or large skillet over medium-high heat. Add the chopped chile and garlic and stir-fry gently for about 2 minutes. Stir in the curry powder and the reserved squash cooking liquid. Add the grapes and the squash flesh to the pan. Season with salt and pepper and cover. Cook over low heat for another 5 minutes.

Drain the rice. Combine all the ingredients, season, and sprinkle with the pumpkin seeds before serving.

PER PORTION: 519 calories • 18 g protein• 19 g fat • 74 g carbohydrates

Spanish Potato
with zucchini, red pepper, and leek
Tortilla

Wash the potatoes and cook unpeeled in a small amount of salted water with the cumin for about 20 minutes, until tender. Drain, cool slightly, and peel. Cut into thick slices.

Wash the zucchini, cut it in half lengthwise, and slice. Halve, trim, and wash the pepper, and chop. Trim the leek, slit it lengthwise, and wash it well. Shake it dry and cut into thin rings.

Heat the oil in a large nonstick skillet over medium-high heat. Sauté the potatoes in the oil until golden brown. Add the sliced zucchini, chopped pepper, and sliced leek, and cook over low heat for about 5 minutes, stirring gently.

Serves 2:
8 oz boiling potatoes
Salt to taste
1 tbs ground cumin
1 small zucchini
1 red bell pepper
1 small leek
2 tbs olive oil
1 red chile
1 small clove garlic
4 eggs
Black pepper to taste

Slit open the chile, remove the seeds, and finely chop the flesh. Peel and chop the garlic. Beat the chile and garlic with the eggs and season with salt and pepper. Pour the egg mixture over the potatoes and vegetables. Cover with a lid and place over very low heat for about 5 minutes, until the eggs are set. Invert onto a cutting board and cut into wedges to serve.

power

PER PORTION: 474 calories • 31 gprotein • 30 g fat • 20 g carbohydrates

Provençal

a light classic from the south of France

Peppers

Soak a small clay pot and lid in water for 15-30 minutes. Meanwhile, halve, seed, and core the peppers. Wash the pepper halves and cut them into strips.

Serves 2:

1 each small red, yellow, and green bell pepper

1 lb beefsteak tomatoes

4 oz zucchini

1 medium onion

1 clove garlic

2 sprigs fresh rosemary

3-4 sprigs fresh thyme

Salt to taste

Black pepper to taste

2 tsp fresh lemon juice

1 tbs olive oil

1/2 cup vegetable stock

Cut an X into the round ends of the tomatoes and place in boiling water for a few moments. Remove them with a slotted spoon, then peel, remove the core, and chop roughly. Wash, trim, and roughly chop the zucchini. Peel and finely chop the onion and garlic. Wash and shake dry the herbs, setting some aside for garnish. Finely chop the rest.

Place the vegetables in the clay pot with the salt, pepper, lemon juice, oil, and stock. Cover with the lid and place in the bottom of a cold oven. Turn on the oven heat to 400°F and bake for about 1 hour. Stir the vegetables, season, and sprinkle with the reserved herbs before serving.

Gentle cooking in a clay pot

Cooking in a clay pot is the perfect way to cook vegetables and retain the maximum amount of vitamins, although they take somewhat longer than when cooked in a saucepan. In clay-pot cooking, the vegetables steam gently in their own juices in a firmly sealed container. A minimum of fat is used, and the vegetables turn out wonderfully light and aromatic.

PER PORTION:

175 calories

6 g protein

6 g fat

24 g carbohydrates

power

Salsify and

with plenty of vitamins B$_1$ and E

Ham Ragout

Thoroughly wash the salsify. Bring a large, wide pot of water to a boil and add the salt and vinegar. Boil the salsify for about 15-20 minutes, taking care not to let it become too soft.

Serves 2:
About 1 lb salsify
Salt to taste
2 tbs white vinegar
1 small onion
1 tbs butter
2 tbs flour
1/2 cup vegetable stock
1/2 cup milk
White pepper to taste
4 oz smoked ham (about 1 thick slice)
1/2 bunch fresh basil

Drain the salsify and rinse under cold water. Either pull off or peel the dark skin (wear rubber gloves), then cut the salsify into 1^1/$_4$-1^1/$_2$-inch lengths.

Peel and finely chop the onion. Melt the butter in a saucepan over medium heat and sauté the onion until translucent. Sprinkle the flour over the onion and cook, stirring constantly, until golden. Gradually add the stock and the milk. Cook, stirring, until slightly thickened, then season well with salt and pepper. Dice the ham. Wash and finely chop the basil. Add both to the pot with the salsify and heat through. Season well.

Salsify

Salsify is easy to digest and contains good amounts of vitamins, such as A (carotene), B$_1$, and E. Diabetics will be interested to learn of its high insulin level–a carbohydrate that poses no problem.

PER PORTION:
274 calories
15 g protein
11 g fat
16 g carbohydrates

power

Stovetop Spelt Cakes
healthy and elegant
with Radishes

Gently toast the spelt in a small dry saucepan over medium heat. Pour in the stock and bring to a simmer. Cover with a lid and simmer for about 10 minutes over low heat, then remove from the heat and let stand until plumped, about 20 minutes.

Serves 2:
3 oz ground spelt
1/2 cup vegetable stock
1 large bunch radishes
1 red onion
2 tbs butter
Salt to taste
Black pepper to taste
2 eggs
1 tbs crème fraîche

Wash and trim the radishes and leaves. Finely chop a few of the tender leaves. Cut the radishes into four or eight pieces each. Peel and finely chop the onion. Melt 1 tbs of the butter in a skillet over medium heat and gently sauté the onion until translucent. Add the radishes and tops. Season well with salt and pepper, then cover and cook over low heat for about 5 minutes. Do not add any more liquid.

Beat the eggs and stir them into the spelt. Season with salt and pepper. Melt the remaining 1 tbs butter in a nonstick skillet over medium heat. Drop small amounts of the spelt mixture into the pan and sauté until golden brown on both sides. Check the flavor of the radish mixture, then arrange on plates on top of the spelt cakes. Add a tiny dollop of crème fraîche to each plate and serve immediately.

PER PORTION: 390 calories • 20 g protein • 18 g fat • 37 g carbohydrates

Carrot Crêpes
with herbed cottage cheese
with Asparagus

To make the crêpes, mix the eggs, salt, water, and flour. Cover and let stand for about 30 minutes.

Wash, trim, and peel the asparagus. Bring a small amount of water to a boil in a saucepan with some salt, 2 tbs of butter, and the sugar. Place the asparagus in a steamer insert and lower it into the saucepan. Cover tightly and steam over low heat for 5-8 minutes, until tender-crisp.

Beat together the cottage cheese, apple syrup or honey, lemon juice, salt, and pepper. Thin the mixture slightly with a little milk. Wash the herbs, shake dry, and chop; add to the cottage cheese mixture. Season well with salt and pepper.

Wash, trim, and peel the carrots. Grate them finely and add to the crêpe batter. In a nonstick skillet, cook two crêpes in succession, melting about 1 tsp butter in the pan for each one; cook until golden brown on both sides. Drain the asparagus, divide into two equal portions, and wrap a crêpe around each portion. Place on plates and serve with the herbed cottage cheese.

Serves 2:
2 eggs
Salt to taste
1/2 cup water
1/3 cup flour
1 3/4 lb white or green asparagus
1/4 cup butter
1 tsp sugar
4 oz low-fat cottage cheese
1/2 tbs apple syrup, or
3/4 tsp honey
1/2 tbs fresh lemon juice
Black pepper to taste
Milk
1/2 bunch mixed fresh herbs
3 oz carrots

PER PORTION: 415 calories • 25 g protein • 17 g fat • 30 g carbohydrates

Turnip and Turkey
great with brown rice
Fricassee

Wash, trim, and slice the turnips and the carrots, halving any large slices. Place the slices in a steamer insert.

Bring a small amount of salted water to a boil in a small saucepan. Place the steamer insert with the vegetables in the saucepan, cover tightly, and steam the vegetables over low heat for about 10 minutes, until still slightly firm to the bite.

Meanwhile, rinse the turkey under cold water, pat dry with paper towels, and cut into small pieces. Wash and shake dry the basil, putting some of the leaves aside as garnish, and finely chop the rest.

Melt the butter in a wide saucepan, add the turkey and sauté until golden brown on all sides. Sprinkle the flour over the turkey, stir to combine, then gradually add the milk and stock. Simmer the sauce gently for 5 minutes over low heat, stirring occasionally, until thickened.

Serves 2:
7 oz small white turnips
7 oz carrots
Salt to taste
7 oz turkey breast
1/2 bunch fresh basil
1 tbs butter
2 tbs flour
1/2 cup milk
1/2 cup chicken stock
Black pepper to taste
Fresh lemon juice to taste
1-2 tbs dried
mushroom powder

Add the prepared vegetables and the chopped basil and return the mixture to a boil. Season the fricassee with salt, pepper, lemon juice, and the dried mushrooms. Garnish with the basil leaves before serving.

PER PORTION: 310 calories • 29 g protein • 6 g fat• 21 g carbohydrates

Stir-Fried
with hot chile and sweet pineapple
Thai Vegetables

Peel and finely chop the garlic and ginger. Slit open the chile and scrape out the seeds. Rinse the chile and slice into thin rings. Wash and trim the broccoli and divide into florets. Peel and chop the broccoli stalks. Wash and peel the carrot and cut diagonally into thin slices. Wash and pick over the bok choy or cabbage, and cut into thick slices. Wash and trim the green onions and cut diagonally into thin slices. Peel the pineapple, remove the core, and cut into small dice.

Heat the oil in a wok or large skillet over medium-high heat. Add the garlic, ginger, and chile rings and stir-fry briefly. Add the broccoli and carrot and stir-fry for about 2 minutes. Add the green onions and stir-fry for 1 minute. Sprinkle the sugar over the vegetables and pour in the stock. Add the bok choy, pineapple, fish sauce, and a squeeze of lime juice and bring to a boil. Serve garnished with cilantro leaves.

Serves 2:

1 clove garlic
Thumb-sized piece fresh ginger
1 red chile
8 oz broccoli
1 carrot
3 oz baby bok choy or
Chinese cabbage
2 green onions
2-3 slices fresh pineapple
1 tbs vegetable oil
2 tsp brown sugar
1/2 cup vegetable stock
2 tbs Thai fish sauce (*nam pla*)
Lime juice to taste
Fresh cilantro leaves

PER PORTION: 235 calories • 8 g protein • 10 g fat • 33 g carbohydrates

Linguine with Raw Tomato Sauce

aromatic and low in calories

Cut an X into the round ends of the tomatoes and place in boiling water for a few moments. Remove from the water, peel, and remove the core and seeds. Chop into small pieces.

Serves 2:
1 lb ripe tomatoes
1 clove garlic
2 tbs fruity extra virgin olive oil
Salt to taste
Black pepper to taste
8 oz linguine
Fresh basil
2 tbs freshly grated Parmesan cheese

Peel and finely chop the garlic. Place in a bowl with the tomatoes and oil, and season with salt and pepper. Cover and set aside.

Cook the linguine in a large amount of boiling salted water until slightly firm to the bite (*al dente*). Drain well in a sieve.

Stir the tomato sauce and taste. Heat through briefly, then combine with the pasta and serve immediately. Wash and dry the basil and sprinkle over the pasta to taste, along with the Parmesan.

Tomatoes

Most pasta sauces are cooked for long periods of time, which reduces their vitamin content. In this briefly cooked sauce, the tomatoes are still bursting with A, C, E, and B complex vitamins when you sit down to eat. Tomatoes are also low in calories, diuretic, and good for the blood.

PER PORTION:

512 calories

18 g protein

12 g fat

81 g carbohydrates

power

Mixed Fresh

with refreshing yogurt cream

Berries

Mix the yogurt with the apple syrup or honey, milk, and a small amount of ground cinnamon, and divide among two dessert plates.

Wash the lemon thoroughly under hot running water and dry well. Finely grate the lemon zest and squeeze the juice. Mix both in a bowl with the sugar. Wash, pick over, and drain the berries and grapes or currants. Wash the plums and remove the stones. Cut the plums into segments. Carefully stir the plum segments into the lemon juice mixture.

Arrange all of the fruit on top of the yogurt, sprinkle lightly with cinnamon, and serve immediately.

Serves 2:

4 oz low-fat plain yogurt
1 tbs apple syrup, or
1/2 tbs honey
2 tbs milk
1/2 tsp ground cinnamon, plus more for garnish
1/2 lemon
1 tbs sugar, or more to taste
2 oz small fresh raspberries
2 oz fresh blackberries
2 oz fresh blueberries
2 oz small seedless red grapes or red currants
2 fresh yellow plums

power

PER PORTION: 173 calories • 4 g protein • 1 g fat • 38 g carbohydrates

Strawberry and
contains plenty of vitamin C
Kiwi Salad

Serves 2: 1/2 lime • 1 tbs maple syrup • Pinch of vanilla powder • 8 oz small fresh strawberries • 2 kiwis • 1-2 tbs pecans (roughly chopped)

Wash the lime under hot running water, grate the zest, and squeeze the juice. Combine the zest and juice with the maple syrup and vanilla. Wash the strawberries briefly, remove the stalks, and cut thickly. Peel and halve the kiwis and cut into slices. Arrange the fruit on plates, pour over the syrup, and top with the pecans.

PER PORTION: 104 calories • 1 g protein • 5 g fat • 15 g carbohydrates

Date and
with lime juice and honey
Pineapple Salad

Serves 2: 1/2 small fresh pineapple • 1 kiwi • 4 fresh dates • 2 tbs fresh lime juice • 2 tsp brown sugar • 1 tbs floral honey • 1 tbs dried coconut (toasted)

Peel the pineapple, cut lengthwise into fourths, and remove the core. Cut into slices, saving as much of the juice as possible. Peel and halve the kiwi and slice the halves. Remove the pits from the dates and cut into segments. Stir together the lime and pineapple juices, sugar, and honey. Mix the juice mixture with the fruit and sprinkle with the toasted coconut.

PER PORTION: 125 calories • 1 g protein • 1 g fat • 31 g carbohydrates

Melon and Mango
refreshing and healthy
Soup with Kiwi

Halve the orange and squeeze the juice. Halve the melon and remove the seeds and fibers. Using a melon baller, scoop several small balls out of the melon flesh; cover and place in the refrigerator. Remove the rest of the melon flesh from the skin. Peel the mango and cut the flesh from the pit. Puree the melon and mango flesh with the orange juice, and strain through a sieve. Flavor the soup with lemon juice and a few drops of bitters, and divide among two chilled bowls.

Halve and peel the kiwi and cut into slices. Place in the soup, together with the melon balls. Garnish with a few lemon balm or mint leaves.

Serves 2:
1 orange, well chilled
1/2 ripe melon, such as cantaloupe, well chilled
1 small ripe mango, well chilled
1-2 tbs fresh lemon juice
Angostura bitters
1 kiwi
Fresh lemon balm or mint leaves

Melons, mangos, and kiwis

All these fruits are very low in calories and very high in vitamins and other "goodies." Melons are diuretic and generally cleansing, so they are an ideal part of any diet or beauty regime. Mangos provide carotene and B complex vitamins; kiwis contain generous amounts of vitamin C.

PER PORTION:

122 calories

2 g protein

1 g fat

31 g carbohydrates

Jellied

with juicy plums

Buttermilk Soup

1 1/2 packages unflavored gelatin
1 cup buttermilk
1/2 cup apple juice
1/2 tsp grated lemon zest
2 tbs apple syrup, or 1 tbs honey
1/2 tsp ground cinnamon
5 oz fresh plums

Pour the buttermilk into a small saucepan and sprinkle with 1 package of gelatin. Let stand for 5 minutes, then heat gently, stirring, to dissolve the gelatin. Cool. Repeat the soaking and dissolving procedure with the apple juice and remaining gelatin.

Mix the buttermilk mixture with the lemon zest, apple syrup or honey, and ground cinnamon. Pour into 2 small soup plates and chill until set. Do not chill the apple juice.

Wash and halve the plums and remove the stones. Arrange the plums on the jellied buttermilk, cut into fan shapes, if desired. Pour over the apple juice and place in the refrigerator to set, covering the plates with plastic wrap to prevent vitamin loss.

Plums

Carotene, B vitamins, and vitamin C are prominent in these fruits, which also contain plenty of minerals. The optimum benefit is gained from the plums' carotene, the precursor to vitamin A, if you slice open the fruit and combine them with a little fat (as in the buttermilk). This recipe is also delicious made with strawberries.

PER PORTION:

207 calories

7 g protein

1 g fat

47 g carbohydrates

Citus Fruit
with creamed cottage cheese
Platter

Wash the lime and lemon in hot water and dry well. Remove some of the zest in fine strips, and finely grate some of the rest. Squeeze the juice of both fruits. Combine the juice and the grated zest with the maple syrup and cottage cheese and mix well.

Peel the orange and the grapefruit, removing all of the bitter white pith. Remove the fruit segments from between the membranes.

Divide the cottage cheese mixture among two plates. Arrange the orange and grapefruit segments decoratively on top. Roughly chop the pecans and sprinkle over the desserts with the chocolate flakes and grated lime and lemon zests.

Serves 2:
1 small lime
1/2 lemon
2 tbs maple syrup
4 oz low-fat cottage cheese
1 large orange
1 large pink grapefruit
1 oz pecans
2 tsp shaved chocolate

Citrus fruits

Whether grapefruit, lime, orange, or lemon, citrus fruits provide lots of beta carotene and vitamin C, and contain large quantities of minerals. Because the vitamins are delicate, you should always eat citrus fruit as soon as you have peeled it. Almost as good: drink a large glass of freshly squeezed juice.

PER PORTION:

332 calories

15 g protein

18 g fat

37 g carbohydrates

Jellied Fruit Tea

a little light relief

with Grapes

Brew the fruit tea in a teapot with the boiling water and steep for 5 minutes. Soak the gelatin in the cold water for 5 minutes.

Wash the lemon in hot water and dry. Finely grate the zest and squeeze the juice. Dissolve the gelatin in the hot tea. Add the lemon juice and zest and 1 tbs of the sugar.

Wash the grapes and set some aside for garnish; halve the remaining grapes and remove the seeds, if necessary. Divide the grapes among two tall glasses and pour over the tea. Cover and refrigerate until set.

Beat the yogurt with the remaining 1 tbs sugar. Pour onto the jellied tea and serve garnished with grapes.

Serves 2:

3 tbs fruit tea leaves

1 cup water

1 package unflavored gelatin

1/2 cup cold water

1/2 lemon

2 tbs confectioners' sugar

3 oz each red and green grapes

3 oz low-fat plain yogurt

Grapes

Grapes are full of glucose, which provides instant energy when consumed. Although the amount of vitamins does not quite compare with the levels in other fruits, grapes are nevertheless valuable. They stimulate the metabolism and the digestive system, detoxify the body, stimulate the reproduction of blood cells, and are generally beneficial to health, looks, and well-being.

PER PORTION:

101 calories

4 g protein

1 g fat

22 g carbohydrates

power

Blueberry and Banana Milk

full of vitamin B_6 and folic acid

Briefly wash, then pick over the blueberries, and drain well. Peel and roughly chop the banana and sprinkle with the lemon juice. Puree the blueberries with the banana and the pear syrup or honey in a blender. Stir in the vanilla and cold milk. Pour into glasses and serve immediately.

Serves 2:

8 oz blueberries

1 small ripe banana

1 tbs fresh lemon juice

1 tbs pear syrup, or

1/2 tbs honey

Dash of vanilla extract

1 1/4 cups ice-cold milk

Blueberries and bananas

Blueberries contain large amounts of the protective substances carotene and vitamin C–reason enough to treat yourself to them as often as you like. Other plus points: the blue coloring and tannic acids present in the skin both aid in blood reproduction and are cleansing.

Although bananas contain more energy-producing qualities than other fruits, they also contain certain vitamins that other fruits do not, especially pantothenic acid and folic acid, which are rarely found in fruits.

PER PORTION:

265 calories

10 g protein

10 g fat

35 g carbohydrates

Raspberry and
berry, berry healthy
Strawberry Shake

Wash and pick over the berries. Use a sharp knife to hull the strawberries.

Puree the berries in a blender and strain through a fine sieve to remove

Serves 2:

3 oz raspberries

3 oz strawberries

2 tbs pear syrup, or 1 tbs honey

Pinch of ground cinnamon

Dash of vanilla extract

1/2 cup low-fat cottage cheese

1/2 cup milk

the seeds.

Add the pear syrup or honey, cinnamon, and vanilla

to the fruit puree. Add the cottage cheese and milk,

pulsing briefly to combine.

Pour the shake into glasses and serve immediately.

Raspberries and strawberries

Just 4 oz of strawberries will give you your daily requirement of vitamin C, the most important vitamin for disease resistance. Its other components make this delicious fruit a popular choice for health and beauty. Strawberries quickly lose their flavor and vitamins, so eat them as soon as possible after picking. Raspberries are almost equally healthy (and sensitive), but do not contain quite the same levels of vitamins.

PER DRINK:

216 calories

15 g protein

8 g fat

22 g carbohydrates

Fruity
best served well chilled
Cucumber Drink

Serves 2: 7 oz cucumber (well chilled) • 2 kiwis (well chilled) • 1/2 tsp ground ginger • Salt to taste • Black pepper to taste • Well-chilled mineral water

Peel and roughly chop the cucumber, then puree in a blender. Peel and roughly chop the kiwis. Add to the pureed cucumber and blend again briefly. Do not process for long, as otherwise the shake will become bitter. Add the ground ginger, salt, and pepper, and pour into tall glasses. Top with well-chilled mineral water and serve immediately.

PER DRINK: 42 calories • 1 g protein • 1 g fat • 10 g carbohydrates

Carrot and
a healthy snack
Tomato Yogurt

Serves 2: 1/2 cup low-fat yogurt • 1 cup tomato juice • 1/2 cup carrot juice • Salt to taste • Black pepper to taste • Pinch of ground cumin • Lime juice to taste • 2 slices of lime

Combine the yogurt with the tomato and carrot juices in a blender and blend for a few seconds. Flavor the drink with salt, pepper, cumin, and a dash of lime juice and pour into glasses. Serve garnished with lime slices.

PER DRINK: 143 calories • 4 g protein • 1 g fat • 10 g carbohydrates

Iced Pineapple and

an exotic burst of vitamins

Almond Shake

Peel the pineapple, removing the brown "eyes." Cut the fruit into fourths lengthwise and remove the hard core from the segments. Roughly chop the fruit and place in a blender.

Serves 2:
1/2 small ripe pineapple
1/2 lime
1 tbs brown sugar
1 tbs unsweetened almond butter
4 oz vanilla frozen yogurt
Crushed ice
1 small kiwi
Fresh mint

Squeeze the juice from the lime and add to the blender with the sugar and almond butter. Puree until smooth. Add the frozen yogurt and blend again briefly, until smooth.

Fill 2 tall glasses with crushed ice and pour in the shake. Cut the kiwi (peeled or unpeeled) into segments or thick slices. Garnish the shakes with the kiwi slices and mint leaves.

Pineapple

This tropical fruit has high levels of vitamins A, B, and C. The flesh contains *bromelin*, an enzyme that separates protein in the body, and thus stimulates the digestion of protein. Incidentally, this enzyme is also responsible for the incompatibility between fresh pineapple and gelatin—it prevents the gelatin from setting. Pineapple contains only a few calories, is diuretic, and detoxifying; it is a useful part of any diet.

PER DRINK:

167 calories

5 g protein

6 g fat

25 g carbohydrates

power

Happy Food

Eat Your Way
with a wide variety of foods
to a Good Mood

NUTRITION AND THE PSYCHE

Everyone has an off day now and then when they might feel a bit depressed. All of our moods—the close interplay of emotions that occurs between our body and soul—are chemically controlled in the brain. The brain does this by using neurotransmitters such as serotonin and endorphins, which are generated as needed at the speed of light. Certain substances in the food we eat are involved in the generation of these neurotransmitters and can hence directly affect our productivity, behavior, and—last but not least—our moods.

PAY ATTENTION TO YOUR BRAIN'S SIGNALS

Good moods are closely linked with an overall feeling of relaxation, and with a rested body. If you are permanently stressed, you cannot expect to feel good in the long run. If you want to maintain a good mood, you should pay attention to the signals from your brain. Don't keep working when you're tired; instead, try to take a break. Energy drinks used as a quick pick-me-up really don't help in such cases—on the contrary, when they wear off, your stress and lack of motivation will be even greater than before.

Mood Enhancers:

* Select foods containing substances that will optimize the processes in your brain and promote the generation of neurotransmitters.
* Make sure to get enough sleep—at least seven or eight hours a night for most people.
* Exercise! Exercise increases the serotonin levels in your brain and boosts the distribution of endorphins.

Mood Detractors:

* Main detractors to a good mood are saturated fatty acids. They need a great deal of oxygen to burn, which means that they impair (among other things) the transportation of oxygen to the brain. That makes you tired, listless, and even causes some people to become depressed. Animal products such as high-fat meats, bacon, sausage, high-fat cheeses, mayonnaise, many sweets, and high-fat pastries (such as cream pies) all contain high levels of saturated fatty acids.
* Increased alcohol consumption also has a negative effect on moods. On one hand, alcohol destroys B vitamins—the precise vitamins we desperately need to generate neurotransmitters. Small amounts of alcohol, however, can occasionally give a good mood a boost.

Brain Food

To ensure that our brain, which centrally controls all the body processes, can successfully meet its wide variety of tasks, it needs the following:

* Sufficient oxygen
* Sufficient energy in the form of glucose, the smallest unit of carbohydrates. Glucose should ideally be derived from whole grain breads, grains, potatoes, fresh vegetables, and fruit.
* Polyunsaturated fatty acids, which ensure that the protective coating of the nerve cells remains functional and that information is transmitted over the nerves as quickly as possible. Excellent sources of polyunsaturated acids are cold-pressed vegetable oils, nuts and seeds, and saltwater fish, such as mackerel, herring, tuna, and salmon.
* Amino acids, the smallest of the protein molecules, form the building blocks for neurotransmitters and hormones. Good sources include fish, shellfish, lean meat, eggs, milk and dairy products, cheese, grains, and legumes.
* A balanced intake of vitamins, minerals, and trace elements are essential for getting the biochemical processes going. These can be found in abundance in fresh vegetables and fruit, in grains and dairy products, lean meat, fish, nuts, seeds, and fresh herbs.

Mood-Enhancing
how to feel better every day
Brain Chemicals

BIOLOGICAL SUBSTANCES THAT MAKE YOU FEEL HAPPY

The neurotransmitters that transport information from one nerve cell to another are either substances that are supplied directly by our bodies or substances that are gained from our diet. Some neurotransmitters must first be generated in the brain. The building blocks for these types of neurotransmitters are usually amino acids, though additional vitamins, minerals, trace elements, or even fatty acids are frequently needed as well. Of the over 60 neurotransmitters discovered thus far, the following help to keep your mood on track:

SEROTONIN

This substance is also referred to as the "good mood hormone" because it plays the lead chemical role in feeling happy. If a sufficient amount is present, we feel balanced and happy. Serotonin promotes relaxation and a feeling of well-being and supports deep sleep. If the brain has an insufficient amount of serotonin, your mood rapidly deteriorates, and a lack of serotonin can even make you aggressive. This neurotransmitter is already contained in some foods, or it can be formed from tryptophan, an amino acid. More serotonin is formed when we consume less fat and more carbohydrates.

ACETYLCHOLINE

This neurotransmitter is synthesized from choline, which is a B vitamin. Among other things, acetylcholine promotes concentration, alertness, learning, and memory. This neurotransmitter keeps us mentally fit, optimistic, and relaxed. Some medications and drugs, however, can significantly disrupt the synthesis and effect of acetylcholine.

DOPAMINE

This neurotransmitter stimulates the heart, circulation, and metabolism. It can mobilize the body's energy sources. As a result, you are active and feel good. Dopamine affects our thoughts, and high concentrations can lead to exaggerated fantasies and brief lapses into daydreams. A huge deficit of dopamine can lead to a lack of motivation and even to emotional voids.

NOREPINEPHERINE

Aside from serotonin, norepinepherine is one of the most important happiness hormones. It has a stimulating effect on the brain, and it promotes perception, motivation, and energy. This neurotransmitter also acts as an antidepressant. New studies show that norepinepherine not only helps you focus in stressful situations, it may even make you feel optimistic and euphoric, which makes stress fun and invigorating. You can also thank norepinepherine for making memories of happy occasions or strong feelings particularly intense. The building block of norepinepherine is the amino acid phenylalanine.

ENDORPHINS AND NEUROPEPTIDES

Endorphins are a group of brain chemicals that act like drugs or natural narcotics. They can ease pain and trigger a sense of well-being as well as happy or euphoric feelings. When the endorphin level rises, it provides for a balanced psyche. Serotonin activates endorphins, while norepinepherine prevents the premature drop of these highly sensitive chemicals. Neuropeptides cause stimulating effects; among other things, they control our emotions as well as sexual behavior and eating patterns.

Foods to Improve
stimulating and invigorating foodstuffs
Your Mood

EATING WELL AND LAUGHING GO HAND IN HAND

Among the various agents in food, there are a handful of substances that can intensify the positive effect of neurotransmitters, which include the following:

❋ Phytochemicals: Phytochemicals are a group of about 30,000 different bioactive, plant-derived substances, such as color, fragrance, and aroma components in foods, especially in fresh fruits and vegetables. They play a substantial role in maintaining a healthy and vital body.

❋ Spices: All spices soothe the soul. Saffron can help to increase a positive sense of well-being, while nutmeg and cinnamon help to brighten moods. The sweet flavor of vanilla releases endorphins, which also promote a sense of well-being.

❋ Capsaicin: This substance is responsible for the spiciness in paprika and chiles. Capsaicin also releases endorphins.

❋ Sinigrin: This substance found in mustard can boost alertness and activity, and hence support your zest for life.

❋ Stimulating agents: These substances are generated through components of oat protein and result in the release of dopamine, which is in turn a precursor to serotonin. These stimulating agents not only promote concentration and productivity, but both oats and oatmeal brighten your moods.

❋ Caffeine: In studies, test subjects indicated that coffee (2 cups a day) gave them a clearer head, more self-confidence, and more energy. Caffeine probably enhances the effect of dopamine and norepinepherine, hormones that promote productivity. An excess of coffee, however, results in the exact opposite effect, making you nervous and jittery.

❋ Cocoa: Cocoa powder in chocolate contains quite a few highly effective substances that ease frustration and lovesickness and heighten the senses. Theobromine, for instance, stimulates the central nervous system, and phenylethylamine raises the serotonin level and has an invigorating effect.

NEURO-TRANSMITTER	HELPS WITH	GOOD SOURCES
Serotonin	Mood swings; cravings for sweets; restlessness; irritability; minor anxiety; sleep disturbances	Pasta, rice, potatoes, whole grains, whole grain bread, nuts, dates, figs, bananas, pineapple, sweets, legumes, tofu, red vegetables, radishes, fennel, dairy products, cheese, saltwater fish, shellfish, lean meats, poultry
Acetylcholine	Impaired concentration and learning; memory strain	Liver, egg yolks, cheese, oatmeal, soy, lecithin, legumes, whole grains, whole-grain breads, nuts, wheat germ, sesame seeds, brewers yeast
Dopamine	Impaired concentration; lack of motivation	Milk and dairy products, cheese, eggs, potatoes, rice, pasta, poultry, meat, fish, shellfish
Norepinepherine	Mental stress; sleep disturbances; depression; lack of concentration; lack of motivation	Milk and dairy products, fish, shellfish, eggs, poultry, meat, whole grains, legumes, red vegetables, spinach, apples, pineapple, nuts, chocolate
Endorphins and Neuropeptides	Stress; pressure to achieve; mood swings; listlessness and depression	Fish, meat, poultry, dairy products, whole grains, pasta, whole-grain breads, honey, bananas, dried fruit, chocolate and other sweets

Power

enhancing happiness through the food you eat

Week

BEATING THE BLUES

What can you do for yourself if you feel sad, tired, and unmotivated? For seven days, enjoy the following recipes. These recipes are both healthy and easy to prepare, and will enhance a good mood. All in all, this week will harmonize your mind, release positive energy, and make you feel happy.

7-DAY PLAN

In our 7-day plan, you will find suggestions for breakfast, lunch, and dinner for every day of the week. Feel free to mix and match meals any way you like, because all the recipes in this book contain the substances we have discussed that promote more balance and vitality. For those of you who are too busy to cook two meals a day, simply select a meal to prepare for dinner. You can always take along the two sandwiches from the breakfast chapter (page 196) for your lunches. Another ideal solution is whole-grain bread with a low-fat cheese, or Mozzarella Papaya Salad on page 207. Any fresh fruit, such as apples, pears, berries, bananas, figs, or pineapple, combined with yogurt or cottage cheese and a few nuts, always makes a good choice that can be enjoyed at work.

NATURAL ACTIVE AGENTS

The following list outlines how you can tailor foods to suit your own special needs:

❋ Protein-rich foods, such as milk and dairy products, fish, shellfish, and lean meat all support productivity and concentration, as do nuts, legumes, and wheat germ.

❋ The following herbs and spices contain stimulating agents: saffron, nutmeg, ginger, pepper, cinnamon, vanilla, peppermint, basil, and parsley.

❋ If relaxation is what you seek, turn to vegetables from the nightshade family, such as potatoes, tomatoes, and bell peppers, or you can indulge in grains, pasta, rice, and green vegetables.

❋ To support strong nerves, think about including the following in your diet: wheat germ, oatmeal, millet, rice, whole-grain bread, almonds, liver, and lean cuts of pork.

❋ To help reduce stress, turn to milk and dairy products, eggs, cheese, fish, lean meat, whole-grain products, potatoes, vegetables, fruit, nuts, and sesame seeds.

Eating Plan for the Week

Monday

* Muesli with Yogurt and Strawberries
* Tangy Tomato-Basil Shake * Zucchini Pancakes with Cured Salmon
* Waldorf Salad with Pineapple

Tuesday

* Turkey Breast Sandwich
* Halibut with a Rice and Vegetable Crust
* Tex-Mex Wrap with Avocado * Apricot-Cream Cheese Gratin

Wednesday

* Walnut-Berry Yogurt
* Mango Lassi with Maple Syrup * Vegetable Curry with Peanuts
* Corn Fritters with Shrimp

Thursday

* Scrambled Eggs with Cheddar, served with whole-grain bread
* Stuffed Potatoes, served with a mixed greens salad
* Creamy Saffron Soup * Pineapple-Papaya Salad

Friday

* Yogurt with Aloe Vera and Grapes
* Baked Tuna with Fennel, served with brown rice
* Couscous Salad with Red Vegetables

Saturday

* Gorgonzola Sandwich
* Vegetable Stew with Millet * Chocolate Mousse
* Beet and Orange Salad, served with multigrain bread

Sunday

* Salmon Mousse, served with a whole-grain toast
* Spicy Chicken with Fresh Mango Sauce * Creamy Citrus Cooler
* Red Lentil and Arugula Salad

Walnut-

with toasted oats

Berry

Yogurt

Serves 2: 1/4 cup rolled oats • 2 tbs walnuts • 12 oz low-fat plain yogurt

• 1–2 tsp floral honey • 4 oz mixed berries

Toast the oats in a small, dry nonstick skillet until golden brown, stirring

constantly. Finely chop the walnuts, then add the nuts and the oatmeal to

the yogurt, and sweeten to taste with honey. Spoon the yogurt into tall

glasses and top off with the rinsed berries.

PER SERVING: 250 calories • 9 g protein • 13 g fat • 24 g carbohydrates

Muesli with Yogurt
naturally sweetened with maple syrup
and Strawberries

Serves 2: 1 banana • 4 oz fresh strawberries • 1/4 cup unsweetened muesli • 2 tbs wheat germ • 1 cup plain yogurt • 2 tsp maple syrup • 1 sprig fresh mint

Peel and slice the banana. Wash, trim, and quarter the strawberries. Arrange the fruit on one half of each plate. Mix the muesli and wheat germ together, then arrange next to the fruit. Pour the yogurt between the fruit and muesli, then drizzle with maple syrup. Garnish the muesli with mint.

PER SERVING: 190 calories • 7 g protein • 3 g fat • 42 g carbohydrates

Yogurt with Aloe Vera
a great source of vitamin C
and Grapes

Serves 2: 8 oz purple grapes • 2 cups plain yogurt • 1/4 cup aloe vera juice • 1 tsp vanilla extract • 2 tbs ground hazelnuts • Sugar or honey to taste • 1 tbs fresh lemon juice

Wash the grapes, remove stems, then cut in half lengthwise, and remove seeds if desired. Set aside. In a bowl, add yogurt and stir the aloe vera juice, vanilla extract, and ground hazelnuts into the yogurt, and add sugar or honey and lemon juice to taste. Fill two small glass bowls, alternating layers of grapes (use two thirds) and the yogurt mixture. Top off with the remaining one third of the grapes.

PER SERVING: 277 calories • 10 g protein • 11 g fat • 37 g carbohydrates

Scrambled Eggs
on hearty whole-grain bread
with Cheddar

Beat the eggs with the milk, salt, and pepper, until the egg mixture is smooth but not foamy. Melt the butter in a nonstick skillet over medium heat.

Add the egg mixture to the pan and cook slowly over low heat. Once it starts thickening, use a spatula to carefully draw the egg mixture from the outer edge into the center.

Wash and trim the bell pepper half, then chop it finely. Sprinkle the cheddar cheese and grated bell pepper over the scrambled eggs and wait for the cheese to melt. The eggs are finished once the mixture has completely thickened, but is still creamy and shiny. Arrange the scrambled eggs on the whole-grain bread slices and serve warm.

Serves 2:

3 eggs

1/4 cup milk

Salt to taste

White pepper to taste

1 tbs butter

1/2 small red bell pepper

1/4 cup grated cheddar cheese

4 slices whole-grain bread, toasted

Eggs

Eggs are among the most nutritious foods. In addition, they are an unusually rich source of fat-soluble vitamins as well as vitamins B2, B12, and folic acid. Lecithin, also contained in eggs, is an important nutrient for the brain and nerves. Tryptophan, an amino acid, is largely responsible for generating serotonin, a chemical that makes you feel good.

PER SERVING:

380 calories

20 g protein

21 g fat

27 g carbohydrates

Salmon
for Sundays and special occasions
Mousse

Cut the smoked salmon into large pieces. Then, using a food processor or blender, finely puree the smoked salmon along with the olive oil, butter, sour cream, salt, pepper, and 1 tbs of the lemon juice. Wash the chives and shake dry, then use kitchen scissors to cut them finely. Cut the salmon fillet into small cubes, then add to the mousse along with the chives. Season to taste with salt, pepper, and the remaining lemon juice.

Refrigerate the salmon mousse until it is ready to serve. Serve the mousse with the crispy, warm whole-grain toast.

Serves 2:
3 oz smoked salmon
1 tbs olive oil
1 tbs soft butter
2 tbs sour cream
Salt to taste
Pepper to taste
1–2 tbs fresh lemon juice
1/2 bunch fresh chives
5 oz salmon fillet, cooked
4 slices whole-grain bread, toasted

Omega-3 fatty acids for the brain

Of all fish, salmon is one of the richest sources of omega-3 fatty acids, which are vital for protecting nerve cells and accelerating their information flow. The amino acids and vitamins in salmon are involved in the generation of many substances that prevent depression and can enhance sensory perceptions. In other words, eating salmon is a pleasure that pays off by both making you feel good and be more motivated.

PER SERVING:
375 calories
32 g protein
19 g fat
18 g carbohydrates

Turkey Breast
a low-fat meal to go
Sandwich

Serves 2: 2 whole-grain rolls • 2 oz English hothouse cucumber • 1/2 red bell pepper • 2 oz cream cheese, softened • Black pepper to taste • 4 leaves romaine lettuce • 2 oz turkey breast, sliced

Split the rolls in half lengthwise. Wash and slice the cucumber. Wash the bell pepper half, trim, and dice finely. Mix the bell pepper into the cream cheese and season to taste with black pepper, then spread on one half of the rolls. Arrange the romaine, cucumber slices, and turkey breast on bottom half of the rolls, then top with the upper half of the rolls.

PER SERVING: 254 calories • 12 g protein • 14 g fat • 23 g carbohydrates

Gorgonzola
with fresh figs and pistachios
Sandwich

Serves 2: 1 tbs shelled pistachios • 2 long whole-grain rolls • 2 fresh, ripe figs • 4 oz Gorgonzola cheese • 4 leaves red leaf lettuce

Coarsely chop the pistachios and briefly toast in a dry nonstick skillet, then set aside to cool. Slice the rolls in half lengthwise. Wash the figs and pat dry. Cut the figs and Gorgonzola cheese into slices. Arrange the lettuce leaves, cheese, and figs on the bottom half of the rolls, sprinkle with the pistachios, then top with the upper halves of the rolls.

PER SERVING: 400 calories • 16 g protein • 19 g fat • 42 g carbohydrates

Ham Salad Sandwich
rich in bioactive agents
with Vegetables

Briefly drain the pickled vegetables in a sieve, then chop as finely as possible. Wash the apple, pat dry, then cut into quarters and remove the core. Chop the apple quarters into fine dice. Trim the fat from the ham, if necessary, then cut the ham into fine dice.

Stir the pickled vegetables, diced apple, and diced ham together in a bowl. Mix in the yogurt and mustard, then season to taste with the pepper. Spread the ham salad mixture onto the bread slices, cut the slices in half diagonally, then garnish with the minced chives and serve.

Serves 2:

About 2 oz mixed pickled vegetables

1 small apple

4 oz cooked ham

2 tbs plain yogurt

Mustard to taste

White pepper to taste

4 slices dark whole-grain bread (such as rye bread)

1 tbs minced fresh chives

The benefits of sour food

Pickled vegetables contain lactic acid bacteria, which have a beneficial effect on our metabolism. These bacteria protect us from harmful bacteria and fungi, thereby preventing infections and strengthening our immune system. This keeps the body healthy and fit.

PER SERVING:

370 calories

20 g protein

11 g fat

47 g carbohydrates

Beet and
rich in serotonin and phytochemicals
Orange Salad

Wash, peel, and dice the beets. Fill a pot with 1/3 cup water and the maple syrup, cover, and simmer the beets for 8-10 minutes over low heat.

Remove the beets from the heat and stir in the lemon juice and the sherry. Cover and refrigerate the beets overnight.

Drain the beets before serving. Peel the oranges, then cut in half, and cut into thin slices. Collect the juice in a bowl and add up to 2 tbs to the beets. Wash and trim the fennel bulb, then cut into paper-thin slices.

Stir together the remaining orange juice with some salt, pepper, and the oil, then drizzle over the fennel slices. Arrange the fennel and orange slices together with the beets on a plate. Coarsely chop the cashews and sprinkle over the salad before serving.

Serves 2:
8 oz small red beets
1 tbs maple syrup
2 tbs fresh lemon juice
2 tbs cream sherry
2 small oranges
1 small bulb fennel (about 5 oz)
Salt to taste
White pepper to taste
1 tbs olive oil
2 tbs cashews

PER SERVING: 250 calories • 6 g protein • 11 g fat • 28 g carbohydrates

Waldorf Salad
a refreshing source of vitamins
with Pineapple

Coarsely chop 2 tbs of the walnuts. Wash and trim the celery, then cut the stalks into a fine dice and mince any of the greens. Peel the celery root, then wash and either grate the bulb or cut it into very fine dice. Immediately mix the celery root with the lemon juice.

Wash and dry the apples, then cut into quarters and remove the core. Cut the apples into fine dice. Add the diced apples to the grated or diced celery root.

Add the milk to the mayonnaise and stir until smooth, then season to taste with pepper. Stir in the celery root-apple mixture, the walnuts, the diced celery, and the celery greens. Cover and refrigerate the salad for one hour. Cut the pineapple into pieces and fold into the salad. Garnish with the remaining nuts and serve.

Serves 2:
3 tbs shelled walnuts
4 oz celery
4 oz celery root (celeriac)
2 tbs fresh lemon juice
2 red apples
2 tbs milk
2 tbs reduced-fat mayonnaise
White pepper to taste
4 oz fresh pineapple

Walnuts

These aromatic nuts are packed with vital nutrients: amino acids, vitamins, minerals, as well as an abundance of unsaturated fatty acids. This powerful combination revitalizes your brain cells, combats fatigue and stress, promotes activity, and keeps you fit. Walnuts enhance your moods and your sense of well-being.

PER SERVING:

237 calories

5 g protein

12 g fat

33 g carbohydrates

Couscous Salad with

particularly rich in serotonin

Red Vegetables

Peel the carrot, onion, and garlic, then cut all into fine dice. Heat the oil in a saucepan over medium-low heat, then add the carrot, onion, and garlic and sauté lightly. Add the vegetable stock, cover, and simmer over low heat for 2 minutes. Stir in the couscous, bring to a boil, then remove the pot from the burner, cover, and let stand for the period of time specified on the package. Drain the couscous if necessary and cool. Wash and trim the tomatoes and bell pepper, then cut into small cubes. Wash the lettuce, shake dry, then tear into small pieces.

Stir together the vinegar, salt, pepper, and olive oil and stir in the vegetables and the lettuce. Season the couscous to taste with the lemon juice, salt, and pepper, then arrange on plates with the vegetables, lettuce, and fresh basil.

Serves 2:

1 carrot
1 small red onion
1 clove garlic
2 tsp vegetable oil
2/3 cup vegetable stock
1 cup couscous
2 small ripe tomatoes
1 small red bell pepper
4 leaves red leaf lettuce
3 tbs white wine vinegar
Salt to taste
Black pepper to taste
1 tbs extra-virgin olive oil
3-4 tbs fresh lemon juice
Fresh basil

Red vegetables

The colors of food as much as their actual nutrients influence the mind. Red symbolizes warmth, strength, and vitality. Vegetables such as tomatoes, red bell peppers, red beets, carrots, red beans, and red cabbage put new life into you, promote optimism and a positive outlook on life.

PER SERVING:

500 calories

13 g protein

14 g fat

79 g carbohydrates

Red Lentil and
with warm goat cheese
Arugula Salad

Serves 2:

2 tsp olive oil

2 tsp chopped fresh rosemary leaves

4 oz red lentils

1 cup vegetable stock

2 green onions

1 bunch of arugula (about 2 oz)

2 tbs white wine vinegar

Salt to taste

White pepper to taste

1 tbs sunflower oil

1 clove garlic

2 small rounds of goat cheese (about 2 oz each)

Heat the olive oil in a saucepan over medium heat and briefly sauté the rosemary. Add the lentils and vegetable stock, cover, and simmer for 10 minutes over low heat. Preheat the oven to 350°F.

Wash and trim the green onions, then cut into thin rings. Trim and sort the arugula leaves, then wash and shake dry before tearing into small pieces. Drain the lentils in a sieve. Stir together the vinegar, salt, pepper, and sunflower oil, then add 2 tbs of the mixture to the warm lentils. Peel and mince the garlic and add it to the lentils. Season the salad with salt and pepper. Score the goat cheese on both sides in the shape of a star. Place the goat cheese in a small oiled baking dish and bake until slightly melted, about 5-10 minutes. Fold the green onions, arugula, and remaining marinade into the lentil salad, then arrange on plates with the warm cheese.

Lentils

Like peas and beans, red lentils are a member of the legume family, are a great source of minerals, and are rich in vitamin B1, which is essential for keeping the brain and muscles fit. Red lentils also have a high content of vegetable protein and are a rich source of tryptophan, the building block of serotonin.

PER SERVING:

395 calories

23 g protein

20 g fat

31 g carbohydrates

Creamy Saffron
with leeks and toasted almonds
Soup

Serves 2:
1 slice whole-grain bread
1 shallot
1 small clove garlic
1 small leek
1 tbs olive oil
1/2 tsp ground saffron
2 1/2 cups vegetable stock
3 tbs heavy cream
Salt to taste
White pepper to taste
1 tbs sliced almonds

Toast the bread and cut it into small cubes. Peel the shallot and garlic, then chop both finely. Thoroughly wash and trim the leek before cutting into rings. Heat the oil in a saucepan over medium heat, then add the leek, garlic, and shallot and sauté for 4 minutes. Remove a generous 1 tbs of the vegetable mixture from the pot and set aside.

Stir the bread cubes and saffron into the saucepan. Add the vegetable stock, bring to a boil, then cover and simmer gently for 30 minutes. Vigorously stir the heavy cream into the soup, then season to taste with salt and pepper.

Toast the sliced almonds in a small, dry, nonstick skillet until golden brown. Ladle the soup into warm bowls. Stir in the reserved vegetables and the toasted almond slices, then serve.

Saffron

Saffron is the most expensive spice in the world. It's made from the stigmas of a Mediterranean crocus, which are hand-picked and dried. Saffron gives dishes a distinctive yellow color and a slightly bittersweet flavor, while its bioactive substances and ethereal oils soothe the soul. Saffron's qualities as an aphrodisiac have been known since ancient times.

PER SERVING:

205 calories

4 g protein

13 g fat

16 g carbohydrates

Yogurt Soup with
tastes great with sesame flatbread
Red Pepper

Cut the bell pepper into quarters, remove the stem, seeds, and ribs, and wash. Cut the quarters crosswise into short, thin strips. Wash and trim the green onions, then cut them diagonally into thin slices. Peel and mince the garlic.

In a nonaluminum saucepan, whisk together the yogurt, meat stock, and egg. While whisking constantly, quickly bring the mixture to a boil over medium heat. Remove the pot from the heat and season with salt and pepper. Stir well occasionally.

Heat the olive oil in a small skillet, then sauté half each of the bell pepper, green onions, and garlic for 3 minutes while stirring constantly. Wash the mint, shake dry, and set aside several leaves for garnish.

Serves 2:
1 red bell pepper
2 green onions
1 clove garlic
8 oz plain whole-milk yogurt
1 cup meat stock (homemade is best)
1 egg
Salt to taste
White pepper to taste
1 tbs olive oil
3 sprigs fresh mint

Chop the remaining mint leaves. Using a hand blender or regular blender, quickly puree the soup, then ladle into warm serving bowls. Mix together the remaining vegetables and the chopped mint and sprinkle over the yogurt soup. Garnish with the reserved mint leaves and serve.

PER SERVING: 180 calories • 9 g protein • 12 g fat • 9 g carbohydrates.

Mozzarella and
with fresh basil and chile oil
Papaya Salad

Slit open the chile, then trim, wash, and cut it into paper-thin strips. Stir the chile with the oil and salt in a bowl and let stand for about 20 minutes.

Cut the mozzarella in half, then cut into very thin slices. Peel the papaya, cut in half lengthwise, and use a spoon to remove the seeds. Cut the papaya halves crosswise into slices. Wash the basil and shake dry, then remove the leaves from the stems.

Decoratively arrange the mozzarella slices, papaya, and basil leaves on two plates and drizzle with the chile oil. Serve with the sunflower bread.

Serves 2:
1 small red chile
3 tbs soybean or canola oil
Pinch of salt
4 oz fresh mozzarella cheese
1 ripe papaya
3 sprigs fresh basil
Sunflower bread for accompaniment

Papaya—exotic power fruit

Papaya contains beta carotene, a substance that protects nerve cells from aggressive oxygen connections. Papain, an enzyme contained in papaya, gets the metabolism going, enhances fitness, and promotes a good mood.

PER SERVING:
450 calories
23 g protein
39 g fat
4 g carbohydrates

Mango Lassi with

a taste of India—rich in vitamins

Maple Syrup

Serves 2: 10 oz low-fat plain yogurt • 6 tbs mineral water • 1/4 cup mango nectar • 3 tbs fresh lemon juice • Maple syrup to taste • Fresh mint leaves

Using a whisk or blender, vigorously whip the yogurt with the mineral water, mango juice concentrate, and lemon juice until foamy. Sweeten the drink to taste with the maple syrup and pour into two tall glasses. Garnish with mint leaves.

PER SERVING: 165 calories • 5 g protein • 3 g fat • 30 g carbohydrates

Fruit Smoothie with

try fresh ginger as a tasty alternative

Wheat Germ

Serves 2: 1 piece honeydew melon (5 oz) • 1/2 banana • Juice from 4 oranges • 2 tbs wheat germ • Pinch of ground ginger

Peel the melon, remove the seeds, and cut into small cubes. Peel and slice the banana. Using a hand blender or regular blender, puree the fruit along with the orange juice, wheat germ, and ground ginger. Pour into two large glasses and serve with large straws.

PER SERVING: 155 calories • 4 g protein • 1 g fat • 31 g carbohydrates

Creamy Citrus
enhances mental fitness
Cooler

Serves 2: 8 oz low-fat kefir or plain yogurt • 7 oz freshly squeezed orange juice • Juice from 1 lime • 2 tbs granulated lecithin (from the health-food store) • 1 tbs honey • 1/4 tsp vanilla powder

With a hand blender or regular blender, vigorously blend the kefir or yogurt, orange juice, and lime juice with the granulated lecithin and two thirds of the honey. Sweeten to taste with the remaining honey. Pour the mixture into two glasses and sprinkle with the vanilla powder.

PER SERVING: 280 calories • 5 g protein • 17 g fat • 23 g carbohydrates

Tangy Tomato-
best served chilled
Basil Shake

Serves 2: 4 ripe tomatoes • 1/2 cup buttermilk • 1 tbs roughly chopped fresh basil • Pinch of sugar • Tabasco sauce to taste

Briefly plunge the tomatoes into boiling water and remove the skins. Remove the stems, and cut the tomato into small pieces. With a hand blender or regular blender, thoroughly puree the tomatoes, the buttermilk, the basil, and the sugar. Season with Tabasco, adding only one drop at a time. Pour the drink into two glasses and serve.

PER SERVING: 77 calories • 4 g protein • 1 g fat • 14 g carbohydrates

Vegetable Curry
spiced with red chiles and fresh ginger
with Peanuts

Cook the rice in the water, according to the directions on the package. Peel the ginger, garlic, and shallots and cut them into fine dice. Slit open the chiles, then trim, wash, and cut into thin rings. Wash and trim the broccoli and separate into small florets. Wash and peel the carrots and slice them diagonally. Cut the bell pepper in half, remove the stem, seeds, and ribs, then wash and cut into strips. Clean and trim the mushrooms and cut into quarters. Heat the oil in a wok or large skillet over high heat. Briefly stir-fry the ginger, garlic, shallots, and chiles. Stir in the curry paste and briefly stir-fry. Gradually add the coconut milk, then stir in the broccoli and carrots and stir-fry about 3 more minutes. Add the remaining vegetables and continue to cook until everything is tender-crisp. Season to taste with salt and lemon juice. Coarsely chop the peanuts, then sprinkle over the curry along with the cilantro leaves. Arrange on plates with the rice and serve.

Serves 2:

1/2 cup basmati rice

1 cup water

1-inch piece fresh ginger

1 clove garlic

2 shallots

1–2 red chiles

8 oz broccoli

2 carrots

1 yellow bell pepper

4 oz mushrooms

1 tbs vegetable oil

2 tsp red curry paste

1 1/4 cups unsweetened coconut milk

Salt to taste

1–2 tsp fresh lemon juice

2 tbs salted peanuts

2 tbs chopped fresh cilantro

PER SERVING: 385 calories • 14 g protein • 12 g fat • 60 g carbohydrates

Corn Fritters
particularly tasty with a green salad
with Shrimp

Drain the corn in a sieve, then, using a hand blender or regular blender, coarsely puree it with 1 heaping tbs of the cottage cheese. Pour the remaining cottage cheese into a cheesecloth-lined sieve and let drain.

Rinse the shrimp, pat dry, and coarsely chop. Wash, peel, and finely grate the carrot. In a bowl, mix the shrimp and grated carrot with the corn. Peel and mince the garlic and add to the bowl. Stir in the egg yolk, grated coconut, salt, pepper, and cornmeal or flour until the batter is uniform. Heat the oil in a skillet over medium-high heat. From the batter, spoon out six fritters into the pan and fry until golden brown on both sides, about 3 minutes per side. Once cooked, place the fritters on paper towels to absorb excess oil.

Serves 2:
4 oz canned corn kernels
1/2 cup cottage cheese
2 oz shrimp, peeled
1 small carrot
1 small clove garlic
1 egg yolk
2 tbs grated unsweetened coconut
Salt to taste
Black pepper to taste
1 tbs cornmeal or flour
2–3 tbs vegetable oil
1 tbs minced fresh Italian parsley

Mix the drained cottage cheese with the parsley. Arrange the fritters on plates, adding a dollop of the cottage cheese mixture to the middle of each fritter, and serve warm.

PER SERVING: 300 calories • 13 g protein • 21 g fat • 16 g carbohydrates

Spaghetti with Broccoli
studded with prosciutto and capers
Cream Sauce

Coarsely chop 1 tbs of the pistachios, then finely chop the rest. Drain the capers well. Wash and trim the broccoli, then separate into florets and blanch in boiling salted water for 3 minutes. Drain the broccoli, immediately plunge into ice-cold water, then drain well in a sieve.

Bring a generous amount of salted water to a boil and cook the spaghetti according to the directions on the package until slightly firm to the bite, al dente. Meanwhile, peel and mince the shallot. Heat the oil in a saucepan over medium heat, add the shallot and sauté briefly. Add half the broccoli, the vegetable stock, the yogurt, and the finely chopped pistachios. With a hand blender or regular blender, puree everything to create a creamy sauce. Season with salt, pepper, and lemon juice. Cut the prosciutto into wide strips. Warm the remaining broccoli florets in the sauce. Drain the spaghetti, then serve in bowls with the broccoli cream sauce and the strips of prosciutto. Garnish with the capers and the coarsely chopped pistachios.

Serves 2:
2 tbs shelled pistachios
1-2 tbs small capers
10 oz broccoli
Salt to taste
8 oz spaghetti
1 shallot
1 tbs vegetable oil
2/3 cup vegetable stock
1/2 cup plain yogurt
Black pepper to taste
2 tsp fresh lemon juice
2 oz prosciutto, thinly sliced

PER SERVING: 590 calories • 28 g protein • 17 g fat • 83 g carbohydrates

Tex-Mex Wrap
supplies a burst of energy
with Avocado

Wash the tomato, remove the stem, and dice. Trim and wash the bell pepper, then cut into fine dice. Wash and trim the celery, then cut into fine dice. Peel the avocado, cut

Serves 2:
1 tomato
1/2 yellow bell pepper
1/2 stalk celery
1 small ripe avocado
1–2 tbs fresh lemon juice
1 tbs plain yogurt
2 tbs minced fresh cilantro or Italian parsley
Salt to taste
Hot pepper sauce to taste
2 flour tortillas (about 6 inches in diameter)

in half lengthwise and remove the pit. Finely dice one half of the avocado, then mash the other half with 1 tbs lemon juice, and the yogurt. Gently mix the mashed avocado with the diced avocado, the diced vegetables, and 1 1/2 tbs of the minced cilantro or parsley. Season to taste with salt, hot sauce, and the remaining lemon juice.

Spoon the filling onto the two tortillas, roll them up, then cover and refrigerate until ready to serve. When you are ready, cut the Tex-Mex wraps in half at a diagonal and arrange on plates. Garnish with the remaining cilantro or parsley leaves.

Versatile wraps

You can serve these Tex-Mex wraps alone or with a large green salad, or serve them as an unusual side dish next to fast-cooking meat, such as chicken, fish, or steak.

PER SERVING:
220 calories
7 g protein
9 g fat
29 g carbohydrates

Vegetable Stew
provides serotonin and iron for more vitality
with Millet

Bring the millet and 2/3 cup of the vegetable stock to a boil, cover, turn off the heat, and let the millet stand for about 20 minutes. Wash and peel the carrots and kohlrabi. Slice the carrots and dice the kohlrabi. Peel the onion and cut into fine dice.

Heat the oil in a saucepan over medium heat. Briefly sauté the carrots, kohlrabi, and onion in the oil, then add the remaining 3 1/3 cups vegetable stock, mustard, bay leaf, and a little salt and pepper. Bring to a boil, cover, reduce the heat to low, and simmer for 10 minutes.

Wash and sort the spinach, remove any large stems, then tear the leaves into pieces. Wash and dice the tomatoes, removing the stems. Add the spinach, tomatoes, and peas to the pot and simmer another 10 minutes. Peel and mince the garlic, and add to the vegetables. Stir in the parsley or chives and the millet, season to taste with salt and pepper, and serve immediately.

Serves 2:
1/3 cup millet
4 cups vegetable stock
8 oz carrots
1 bulb kohlrabi
1 onion
2 tbs olive oil
1–2 tsp hot mustard
1 bay leaf
Salt to taste
Pepper to taste
Handful of fresh spinach leaves
2 tomatoes
5 oz frozen peas
1 clove garlic
3 tbs chopped fresh Italian parsley or chives

Millet

This small, yellow grain is packed with important nutrients. Millet is a rich source of iron, manganese, copper, magnesium, fluorine, silicic acid, B-vitamins, and lecithin, which makes it a great brain food. This powerhouse grain enhances alertness, vitality, and your overall mood.

PER SERVING:

430 calories

12 g protein

15 g fat

60 g carbohydrates

Zucchini Pancakes
quickly restores lost energy
with Cured Salmon

In a bowl, combine the eggs, flour, pinch of salt, and thyme and stir into a thick batter using a wire whisk. Cover the bowl and refrigerate for 15 minutes. Peel the shallot and cut into very fine dice. Wash and trim the zucchini, then coarsely grate it using a vegetable grater. Stir the shallot and grated zucchini into the batter along with the heavy cream, then season with salt and pepper.

In a large skillet, heat the oil over medium heat. From the batter, spoon about 6-8 portions of the batter into the hot oil and fry until golden brown (about 3 minutes per side), then set aside onto paper towels to absorb any excess oil.

Cut the salmon into wide strips and arrange on plates with the zucchini pancakes. Stir together the yogurt and lime juice and drizzle over the salmon strips.

Serves 2:
2 eggs
1/3 cup flour
Salt to taste
1 tsp dried thyme
1 shallot
8 oz zucchini
2 tbs heavy cream
Black pepper to taste
2–3 tbs vegetable oil
2 oz cured salmon (such as gravlax)
3 tbs low-fat plain yogurt
2-3 tsp fresh lime juice

PER SERVING: 420 calories • 18 g protein • 24 g fat • 33 g carbohydrates

Green Vegetables with Tuna Sauce

full of relaxing calcium and magnesium

Wash and trim the vegetables. Peel the lower third of the asparagus stalks. Cut the zucchini in quarters lengthwise, and cut the celery in half lengthwise. Cut the asparagus, zucchini, celery, and green onions into pieces roughly the size of the green beans.

Wash the lime in hot water, pat dry, then grate the zest and squeeze the juice. Add the vegetables to a shallow bowl, lightly salt and pepper, and sprinkle with the lime zest. Wash the parsley and set aside three sprigs.

Pour the water into a wide saucepan, then add 1/2 tsp salt, and the asparagus. Place a steamer rack on top of the asparagus and set the shallow bowl on a steam rack. Cover the pot and steam the vegetables for 10-12 minutes, until tender-crisp.

Drain the tuna, then finely puree with the crème fraîche and 2 tbs lime juice. Mince the parsley and stir it into the sauce along with the capers. Season the sauce to taste and serve with the vegetables.

Serves 2:
28 oz mixed green vegetables (such as asparagus, zucchini, celery, green beans, green onions, snow peas)
1 lime
Salt to taste
White pepper to taste
3 sprigs fresh Italian parsley
3/4 cup water
1 small can water-packed tuna (3 oz)
1 tbs crème fraîche
2 tsp small capers

Green vegetables for more vitality

Some say that green is the color of hope. If you're feeling run-down, you should treat yourself to green vegetables, whether raw or carefully cooked to preserve their invigorating vitamins and nutrients. Green vegetables calm, relax, and reduce aggression.

PER SERVING:

235 calories

24 g protein

14 g fat

30 g carbohydrates

Stuffed
with spicy almond-spiked spinach
Potatoes

Thoroughly wash the potatoes under running water using a brush, then boil unpeeled for 30 minutes. Wash and sort the spinach, and remove any large stems. Add the wet spinach to a skillet and wilt over high heat. Transfer the spinach to a sieve, press out most of the liquid, then chop coarsely. Wash the zucchini half and grate coarsely. Peel and dice the onion. Preheat the oven to 425°F. Heat the oil in a skillet over medium heat. Add the onion and grated zucchini and sauté for 2 minutes. Drain the potatoes, then cut in half lengthwise and scoop out some of the flesh to create a cavity, saving the scooped-out potato in a bowl.

Mash the scooped-out potato with the spinach, the onion-zucchini mixture, the egg, Gorgonzola cheese, almonds, and yogurt. Season the filling with salt and pepper. Fill the potato shells with the spinach mixture, dividing evenly. Arrange the filled potatoes on a baking sheet and bake in the middle of the oven for about 15 minutes, until hot.

Serves 2:
3 large boiling potatoes
(about 7–9 oz each)
8 oz fresh spinach
1/2 zucchini
1 onion
2 tbs olive oil
1 egg
About 2 oz Gorgonzola cheese
1/4 cup almonds, very finely chopped
2-3 tbs plain whole-milk yogurt
Salt to taste
Pepper to taste

Potatoes

Along with vitamins, minerals, and fiber, potatoes also contain phenylalanine, an amino acid that is a precursor to norepinepherine, one of the most important happiness hormones. Norepinepherine refreshes and motivates, strengthens nerves and provides a feeling of well-being.

PER SERVING:

645 calories

24 g protein

34 g fat

62 g carbohydrates

Potatoes with Tomato-

with invigorating exotic spices

Yogurt Sauce

Mix the spices together. To prepare the sauce, wash and halve the tomatoes, remove the stems and seeds, and cut into a small dice. Mix the yogurt with the diced tomatoes and one quarter of the spice mixture.

Wash the cilantro or parsley, shake dry, remove the leaves from the stems, and mince the leaves. Mix half of the minced cilantro or parsley into the tomato-yogurt mixture. Season the sauce with salt and pepper, cover, and refrigerate.

Thoroughly wash the potatoes under running water using a brush, then dry and cut the unpeeled potatoes into quarters. Peel the shallots and cut into quarters lengthwise. Heat the oil in a large skillet over medium heat. Add the potatoes and shallots and sprinkle with the remaining spice mixture.

Sauté the potatoes and shallots for about 10 minutes, stirring frequently, then reduce the heat and sauté for about 20 more minutes until tender, turning occasionally. Season the potatoes to taste with salt and pepper. Garnish with the remaining cilantro or parsley and serve with the tomato-yogurt sauce.

Serves 2:
1 tsp ground coriander
1 tsp ground cumin
1/4 tsp ground cardamom
2 dashes ground ginger
Dash each of: ground allspice, cinnamon, and turmeric
Dash of ground nutmeg
2 tomatoes
3/4 cup plain whole-milk yogurt
5 sprigs fresh cilantro or Italian parsley
Salt to taste
Pepper to taste
Generous 1 lb firm potatoes
4 shallots
1 tbs vegetable oil

PER SERVING: 280 calories • 8 g protein • 11 g fat • 38 g carbohydrates

Halibut with a Rice and Vegetable Crust

high in easily digestible protein and fiber

Cook the rice in the water, according to the directions on the package.

Preheat the oven to 400° F. Wash the halibut fillets in cold water, pat dry, season with salt and pepper, and drizzle with the lemon juice. Oil a flat ovenproof pan.

Wash the leek and the carrot. Trim the leek, peel the carrot, and cut both into very thin strips or into cubes. Heat the butter in a skillet over medium heat until it bubbles, then add the vegetables and sauté for 2 minutes. Season with salt and pepper. Drain the rice if necessary. Gently stir the rice, parsley, and cheese into the vegetable mixture.

Arrange the halibut fillets next to each other in the ovenproof pan. Spread the rice and vegetable mixture over the halibut, dividing evenly and patting down slightly. Bake the fish in the middle of the oven for 20–25 minutes until a light crust has formed and the fish is cooked through. Garnish with the lemon slices, watercress and herbs and serve.

Serves 2:
1/4 cup brown rice
2 halibut fillets (about 4 oz each)
1/2 cup water
Salt to taste
White pepper to taste
1 tbs fresh lemon juice
Oil for the pan
1/2 leek
1 carrot
1/2 tbs butter
1 tbs minced fresh Italian parsley
2 tbs grated Swiss cheese
4 thin lemon slices
Watercress or parsley leaves

PER SERVING: 520 calories • 10 g protein • 14 g fat • 50 g carbohydrates

Herbed Mackerel

with valuable fatty acids and nutrients

in Foil

Preheat the oven to 350°F. Rinse the mackerels and pat dry. Season all sides with salt, pepper, and lemon juice and sprinkle with 3 tbs of the dill.

Serves 2:
2 mackerel fillets
Salt to taste
White pepper to taste
2 tsp fresh lemon juice
6 tbs minced fresh dill
3/4 cup sour cream
1/4 cup milk
2 tbs cream-style horseradish
1 tbs capers
1–2 tsp sweet mustard

Place the fillets next to each other on two large sheets of aluminum foil (shiny side up). Fold the foil around the fish to make a tightly sealed package. Prick a hole in the top for a steam vent. Place on an unheated rack and bake the fish in the middle of the oven for 20 minutes.

Beat the sour cream with the milk and the horseradish until creamy. Finely chop the capers and fold into the mixture. Season the mixture to taste with mustard, salt, and pepper. Gently stir in the remaining 3 tbs dill. Serve the horseradish-caper cream with the herbed mackerel.

Mackerel

Mackerel is a true fitness fish. Its high content of potassium, iodine, nerve-strengthening niacin, vitamins D, B6, B12, valuable amino acids, and omega-3 fatty acids all provide for a turbo effect that lightens your mood and gives you power.

PER SERVING:

437 calories

42 g protein

26 g fat

8 g carbohydrates

Baked Tuna
nutrients that invigorate the senses
with Fennel

Rinse the tuna, pat dry, and place on a plate. Drizzle the tuna with lemon juice and 1 tbs of the anise liqueur, then refrigerate. Preheat the oven to 425°F. Wash and trim the fennel bulbs, cut in half, and then cut into thin slices. Set aside the fennel fronds.

Peel the shallot and finely chop. Oil an ovenproof pan. Arrange the fennel, shallot, and oregano in the pan, then season with salt and pepper and drizzle with 2 tsp oil. Pour in the vegetable stock and the remaining anise liqueur.

Bake the fennel in the middle of the oven for 15 minutes, stirring the fennel once halfway through. Wash the tomatoes, remove the stems, and dice. Season the fish with salt and pepper, then arrange on top of the fennel. Spread the diced tomatoes over the fish, and arrange dabs of butter on top. Bake for about another 15 minutes, until the fish is cooked through. Chop the fennel fronds and sprinkle over the fish.

Serves 2:

2 fresh tuna fillets (about 4 oz each)

1 tbs fresh lemon juice

1/4 cup anise liqueur (such as Pernod or ouzo)

12 oz small fennel bulbs

1 shallot

Oil for the pan

2 sprigs fresh oregano

2 tsp olive oil

Salt to taste

Black pepper to taste

2/3 cup vegetable stock

3 tomatoes

1 tbs butter

Fennel

Fennel has a beneficial effect on the mind and body. Calcium, one of its nutrients, plays an important role for nerves and the brain. Iron is essential for a good oxygen supply and fennel's ethereal oils calm and relax the mind.

PER SERVING:

690 calories

49 g protein

40 g fat

20 g carbohydrates

Curried Fish

exotic, hearty, & truly satisfying

Soup

Serves 2:
1 small zucchini
2 small red bell peppers
2 tbs vegetable oil
9 oz firm potatoes
1 shallot
1 clove garlic
2 tbs grated unsweetened coconut
1–2 tsp curry powder
2 cups vegetable stock
1 2/3 cups fish stock or clam juice
Salt to taste
8 oz perch or other mild white fish fillets
4 large shrimp, peeled and deveined
Fresh dill leaves

Wash and trim the zucchini, then cut into small dice. Cut the bell peppers in half, then remove the stems, seeds, and ribs. Wash the halves and cut into small dice. Heat 1 tbs of the oil in a saucepan over medium heat, add the diced vegetables, and sauté for 1 minute. Afterward, transfer the vegetables to a plate, cover, and set aside. Wash, peel, and dice the potatoes. Peel the shallot and garlic, and cut both into fine dice.

Heat the remaining 1 tbs oil in the saucepan over medium heat, add the potatoes, shallot, and garlic and sauté briefly. Stir in the grated coconut and curry powder and sauté lightly with the vegetables. Pour in the vegetable stock, cover, and simmer for 10 minutes over low heat. Add the reserved vegetables, the fish stock, and a little salt, cover, and simmer for 5 minutes over low heat. Rinse and pat dry the fish and shrimp. Cut the fish into pieces (not too small). Remove about 1/4 of the vegetables from the stock and puree in a blender or food processor. Add the puree back to the soup along with the fish and shrimp. Cover and cook over low heat for about 4 minutes, or until the fish is just cooked through. Season the soup to taste, garnish with dill leaves, and serve.

PER SERVING: 390 calories • 31 g protein • 17 g fat • 27 g carbohydrates

Lamb Kebabs with

rich in protein and carbohydrates

Sesame Rice

Score the tops of the tomatoes, then blanch for several seconds in boiling water. Lift out the tomatoes, remove the skins, stems, and seeds, then cut the tomato flesh into small pieces. Peel the garlic and onion, then cut into fine dice. Heat 2 tsp of the oil in skillet over medium heat and sauté the garlic and onion until translucent. Add the tomatoes, salt, pepper, and maple syrup, then cover and simmer gently for 20 minutes. Cook the rice in the water, according to the directions on the package. Cut the meat into bite-sized cubes. Cut the bell pepper in half, remove the stem, seeds, and ribs, then wash and cut into pieces slightly larger than the meat cubes. Thread the meat and bell pepper onto the soaked skewers, alternating between the two.

Heat the broiler. Place the kebabs on a broiling pan and broil about 4 inches from the heat source for about 4 to 6 minutes, turning once, for medium-rare meat. Season the kebabs with salt and pepper. Toast the sesame seeds in a dry nonstick skillet and mix into the rice. Stir the capers into the tomato sauce and season to taste. Serve the kebabs on the rice and accompany with the sauce.

Serves 2:
18 oz ripe tomatoes
1 clove garlic
1 small onion
1 1/2 tbs olive oil
Salt to taste
Black pepper to taste
1 tsp maple syrup
3/4 cup long-grain rice
1 1/2 cups water
10 oz lamb shoulder
1 yellow bell pepper
2 tbs sesame seeds
1 tbs capers

Sesame seeds

Sesame seeds promote fitness and keep you young. Nutrients include calcium, selenium, silicic acid, and lecithin.

PER SERVING:

585 calories

41 g protein

15 g fat

71 g carbohydrates

Honey-Marinated
with zucchini and sun-dried tomatoes
Rump Steaks

Stir together the olive oil, thyme, honey, and a pinch of pepper. Peel and mince the garlic, and add it to the honey mixture. Pat dry the rump steaks, brush all sides with the marinade, cover and marinate in the refrigerator for 2 hours.

Drain the tomatoes in a sieve, taking care to save the oil. Wash and trim the zucchini, cut in half lengthwise, then slice. Cut the tomatoes into strips. Remove the steaks from the marinade and let drain. In a nonstick skillet over medium-high heat quickly sear the steaks for 2 minutes on each side. Salt the steaks, remove from the pan, cover and keep warm. Slowly add the remaining marinade to the pan. Add the zucchini slices, tomato strips, and the oil from the tomatoes to the pan and sauté for 3 minutes, stirring constantly. Season the vegetables with salt, pepper, sugar, and vinegar. Serve the vegetables with the steaks.

Serves 2:
2 tbs olive oil
1/2 tsp dried thyme
2 tsp floral honey
Black pepper to taste
1 clove garlic
2 rump steaks (about 5 oz each)
2 oz oil-packed sun-dried tomatoes
10 oz zucchini
Salt to taste
Pinch of sugar
1–2 tbs balsamic vinegar

PER SERVING: 585 calories • 41 g protein • 15 g fat • 71 g carbohydrates

Spicy Chicken with
a light and fruity dish from South America
Fresh Mango Sauce

Peel the mango and cut away the fruit from the large flat seed in wide strips. Cut the mango strips into pieces and drizzle with lemon juice. For the sauce, finely puree one third of the mango pieces with the yogurt in a blender or food processor. Wash the lettuce leaves, shake dry, and tear into large pieces. Slit open the chile, trim, and cut into thin rings. Rinse and pat dry the chicken and cut into finger-width strips. Heat the oil in a nonstick skillet over medium-high heat, add the chicken strips and chile and sauté on all sides for about 4 minutes until golden brown and cooked through. Season with salt. Arrange the chicken and chile, the lettuce, and the mango pieces on plates and drizzle with the mango sauce. Serve with tortilla chips.

Serves 2:
1 ripe mango
2 tbs fresh lemon juice
2 oz plain whole-milk yogurt
4 leaves leaf lettuce
1 red chile
10 oz boneless, skinless chicken breast
2 tbs vegetable oil
Salt to taste
About 2 oz tortilla chips

Chicken

Chicken is low in fat and easy to digest, and it is also an excellent source of vitamins, minerals, and valuable amino acids, which are necessary for generating neurotransmitters. This combination supplies energy and motivation, and also enhances your sense of well-being.

PER SERVING:

395 calories

32 g protein

17 g fat

27 g carbohydrates

Chocolate

with cardamom and coffee liqueur

Mousse

Break 3 oz of the chocolate into pieces and melt in a bowl placed in a warm water bath, then let cool until lukewarm. Dissolve the espresso in the hot water, then stir in the coffee liqueur and cardamom.

Separate the egg. In separate bowls, beat the egg white and the heavy cream until stiff. Combine the egg yolk, vanilla extract, confectioners' sugar, and lukewarm water and beat until creamy and the sugar is completely dissolved. Gradually stir in the espresso-cardamom mixture, then the lukewarm chocolate. Then fold in the whipped cream, and finally the egg white. Spoon the mousse into two dessert glasses, cover, and refrigerate for at least 2 hours or overnight. Using a vegetable peeler, shave the remaining chocolate and sprinkle over the mousse. Serve with the strawberries, if desired.

Serves 2:

4 oz bittersweet chocolate
2 tsp instant espresso
2 tbs hot water
2 tbs coffee liqueur
1/2 tsp ground cardamom
1 egg
1/3 cup heavy cream
1/2 tsp vanilla extract
1 tbs confectioners' sugar
1 tbs lukewarm water
Sliced fresh strawberries

Choosing chocolate

It can't be denied that chocolate helps with life's frustrations, but ideally you should choose as dark a chocolate as possible; the higher the percentage of cocoa and the lower the percentage of sugar, the better off you'll be. In the end, it isn't the quantity you consume that is important, but rather that you enjoy chocolate dishes slowly and consciously.

PER SERVING:

455 calories

7 g protein

30 g fat

39 g carbohydrates

Mascarpone-
with Italian almond cookies
Cherry Trifles

Serves 2:
2 tbs sliced almonds
8 oz mascarpone cheese
Pinch of vanilla powder
2 tbs sugar
1/4 cup milk
8 oz sweet cherries
About 2 oz amarettini (small Italian almond cookies)
2 tbs cream sherry

Toast the sliced almonds in a small nonstick skillet until golden brown, stirring constantly. Immediately remove from the heat and set aside to cool. Using a wire whisk, beat the mascarpone cheese, vanilla, sugar, and milk in a bowl until creamy, then cover and refrigerate.

Wash the cherries, dry carefully, then remove the stems and pits. Using a knife, lightly crush the cookies into large pieces, then drizzle with the sherry. Spoon loose layers of the mascarpone cream, the crushed cookies, and the cherries into two tall glasses. Garnish with the sliced almonds.

Cherries

Sweet cherries are the best type of cherries for eating. They contain more minerals and trace elements than sour cherries. The darker the color of a fruit, the riper and more aromatic it is.

Per Serving:

735 calories

9 g protein

59 g fat

37 g carbohydrates

Yogurt-Berry
refreshing and invigorating
Parfait

In a saucepan, bring a few inches of water to a boil. In a heatproof mixing bowl, whip the egg yolks, honey, sugar, and ginger until creamy. Place the bowl in the hot water bath (no longer boiling) and briskly whip the batter with a wire whisk until it forms a thick froth. Remove from the hot water bath and continue to beat while the batter cools.

In another bowl, whip the cream until stiff. First fold the whipped cream into the egg yolk mixture, then fold in the yogurt. Spoon the mixture into 2 bowls or parfait glasses, cover, and place in the freezer for at least 3 hours.

About 20 minutes before serving, remove the parfait from the freezer. Sort and wash the berries and pat dry. Garnish the parfait with berries and dust with confectioners' sugar.

Serves 2:

2 egg yolks

3 tsp honey

1 tbs sugar

2 pinches ground ginger

1/3 cup heavy cream

2 oz low-fat plain yogurt

9 oz strawberries or raspberries

Confectioners' sugar

Honey

Honey is effective on many levels. Its chromium promotes the utilization of glucose in the brain, which also supplies energy. Acetylcholine accelerates the transmission of signals between nerve cells, and the smooth consistency of honey releases soothing reflexes in the nervous system.

PER SERVING:

335 calories

7 g protein

19 g fat

35 g carbohydrates

Figs with Frothy
with a relaxing fragrance
Cinnamon Sauce

Serves 2:
1 small orange
3 ripe figs
1 egg yolk
1 tbs confectioners' sugar
2 pinches ground cinnamon
1/2 cup milk

With a long sharp knife, carefully remove the peel from the orange, taking care to remove the white pith. Cut between the fruit's membranes to remove the orange "fillets;" make sure to remove the seeds and collect the juice that escapes. Place 3 sections of orange in a sieve and mash with a spoon, catching the resulting juice and mixing it with the other juice (you should have about 1/4 cup of juice). Carefully wash the figs, pat dry, and slice. Place the fig slices in a bowl, drizzle with 2 tbs of the orange juice, cover, and set aside.

In a saucepan, bring a few inches of water to a boil. In a heatproof mixing bowl, whisk the egg yolk with the confectioners' sugar, cinnamon, and the remaining 2 tbs orange juice until creamy. Place the bowl over the hot water bath (no longer boiling) and add the milk. Vigorously beat the mixture with a wire whisk until a frothy sauce is formed.

Arrange the figs, remaining orange fillets, and the cinnamon sauce in bowls and serve immediately.

Figs

Make sure to buy truly ripe figs. Only figs that are ripe have that unmistakable aroma and fragrance. This fruit tastes best when chilled. If you don't wish to eat the skin, you can also carefully peel the figs.

PER SERVING:
135 calories
4 g protein
5 g fat
17 g carbohydrates

Pineapple-
with lime juice and sesame brittle
Papaya Salad

Serves 2: 2 tbs sesame seeds • 2 tbs sugar • 1 tsp vegetable oil • 1/4 fresh pineapple • 1 kiwi • 1 small ripe papaya • 2 tbs fresh lime juice • Pinch of vanilla powder

In a dry nonstick skillet, brown the sesame seeds and sugar, stirring constantly. Pour the mixture onto an oiled sheet of aluminum foil and let cool. Peel the pineapple, cut in half lengthwise, and cut into pieces. Peel the kiwi and papaya. Cut the papaya in half lengthwise and remove the seeds. Slice the kiwi and papaya. Stir together the lime juice and vanilla, then coat the fruit in the juice. Crumble the sesame brittle and sprinkle over the salad.

PER SERVING: 165 calories • 2 g protein • 5 g fat • 39 g carbohydrates

Dates with
tastes best when chilled
Minted Yogurt

Serves 2: 8 oz low-fat plain yogurt • 2 sprigs fresh mint • 2 tbs sugar • 1/2 tsp vanilla extract • 1 tbs chopped hazelnuts • 2 tbs fresh lemon juice • 8 fresh dates

Pour the yogurt into a cheesecloth-lined sieve, suspend the sieve over a bowl, and let it drain for 30 minutes in the refrigerator. Transfer the yogurt to a bowl. Wash the mint and dry, remove the leaves from the stems and chop coarsely. Place the mint, sugar, vanilla, and nuts in a food processor and process until fine. Stir the mint mixture into the yogurt and add lemon juice. Wash and dry the dates, remove the pits and cut lengthwise into pieces. Serve dates with the minted yogurt for dipping.

PER SERVING: 249 calories • 7 g protein • 5 g fat • 48 g carbohydrates

Apricot-Cream
garnished with pistachios
Cheese Gratin

Preheat oven to 425°F. Wash the apricots, dry well, then cut in half and remove the pits. Cut the fruit into thick wedges and drizzle with the apricot liqueur.

Separate the egg. Beat the egg white until stiff. Mix the cream cheese with the sugar, vanilla, and egg yolk until smooth. Fold the egg white into the cream cheese mixture. Lightly butter 2 small gratin dishes, then pour the cream cheese mixture into the pans and fan out the apricot wedges on top.

Bake the gratin in the middle of the oven for 10 minutes, then increase the oven heat to 475°F. Bake for an additional 5 minutes until the surface of the gratin is golden brown. Garnish with pistachios and serve warm.

Serves 2:

8 oz fresh apricots

1 tbs apricot liqueur

1 egg

2 tbs confectioners' sugar

1/2 tsp vanilla extract

4 oz cream cheese, softened

1/2 tsp soft butter

1 tbs chopped pistachios

Easy to adapt

Depending on the season and your appetite, you can easily substitute other fruits in this dessert. Other tasty choices include bananas, figs, pineapple, oranges, berries, and cherries. You can also use a mixture of fruits.

PER SERVING:

365 calories

9 g protein

25 g fat

24 g carbohydrates

Index

Credits

Published originally under the titles Forever Young:
Fitnß-Drinks plus Eiweiß, Fitness Food, Vitamin Diät:
Natürliche abnehmen mit Obst and Genuss.
Rezepte Fuer Gute Laune

©1999-2000 Gräfe und Unzer Verlag

Authors: Dr. Ulrich Strumz, Dorris Muliar.
Angelika Ilies. Marlisa Szwillus

Photographer: Matteo Manduzio and StockFood Eising, Munich

ISBN: 1-59637-011-4

Printed in China

Caution
The techniques and recipes in this book are to be used at the
reader's solediscretion and risk. Always consult a doctor before
beginning a new eatingplan.

Notes and Recipes

Notes and Recipes

Notes and Recipes